*A*
*Harlequin*
*Romance*

OTHER
*Harlequin Romances*
by ISOBEL CHACE

# CADENCE
# OF PORTUGAL

by

## ISOBEL CHACE

HARLEQUIN BOOKS

TORONTO
WINNIPEG

Original hard cover edition published in 1972
by Mills & Boon Limited, 17 - 19 Foley Street,
London, W1A 1DR, England

© Isobel Chace 1972

SBN 373-01698-0

Harlequin edition published July 1973

Printed in Canada

1698

# CHAPTER I

Camilla Armstrong looked at her brother with a touch of irritation.

'I don't much like children,' she said diffidently. 'I don't know anything about them—'

'Would it matter for a fortnight?' her brother laughed at her.

Camilla pursed up her mouth. 'We shouldn't both be away from the business at the same time,' she protested.

'Oh, come on!' Dennis retorted. 'You carry on as though we were still building up Camilla Enterprises, my dear. The truth is that we've arrived! You've got the golden touch and you know it! A fortnight away from the drawing board isn't going to bankrupt us!'

'N-no,' Camilla admitted.

'Besides,' Dennis went on quickly, sensing that she was weakening, 'your only brother doesn't get married every day!'

'No,' Camilla said again, 'but I wish you'd fallen in love with a nice girl instead of with—'

'A widow and a foreigner?' he supplied for her.

She nodded uneasily. 'I want you to have the very best,' she explained.

'Leonor is the very best for me!'

'And what about the boy?'

'What about him?'

'W-won't you find it difficult to be a father to him?'

Dennis grinned. 'I hadn't thought of that! No, I won't find it difficult. He's very like his mother!'

'But he did have a father—'

'Poor little beggar!' Dennis cut her off, frowning. 'He had a father all right! One of the old nobility, no

less.  He used to come down to the old part of Lisbon
and sing *fado* as an amateur.  Leonor says there are
almost as many rich amateur singers as there are in the
fishing community.  Anyway, he saw Leonor and
married her.  His family wouldn't have anything to do
with her, not even when he was killed, so I reckon
they've forfeited their right to any interest in the child.
He's all Leonor's!'  A faint smile touched his lips.
'It'll do you good to have a break, Camilla.  You might
even find that you like the kid.'

'I might,' Camilla said in unconvinced tones.

'Besides, you'll like Portugal.'

'Will I?'

'Wait until you see it!  It will give you a whole lot
of new ideas for fabrics and so on.  They have the most
fantastic tiles in the older parts of Lisbon.  I'd like you
to see them anyway because I think they might be just
the touch you need for the new collection.  Lots and lots
of formal patterns on dressed cotton would go like a
bomb!'

Camilla was immediately interested.  Anything to do
with work interested her.  A faint flush of colour betrayed her excitement.

'The boy won't want to look at tiles,' she said doubtfully.

'Luis?  He will, you know.  He has a good eye for
design himself—which is more than Leonor has!  She
has the most fantastic black hair, but she hasn't got a
clue as to how to dress!'

Camilla laughed.  'Then what was it about her that
caught your eye?' she asked curiously.  Dennis was
always as well-groomed as she was herself, with the
same cool, fair good looks.  Camilla always looked cool,
calm and collected, even when she was launching some
new line to do with fashion or design on which she had
built up Camilla Enterprises with the help of her

brother.

Dennis shrugged. 'I wanted to listen to some *fado* singing before I left Lisbon. And there she was—dressed totally in black, with a black fisherwoman's shawl over her shoulders. A black bundle with that fantastic voice! I'd never heard anything like it!'

Camilla sighed. 'Oh, all right,' she said. 'I'll look after Luis while you and Leonor have some time to yourselves, but don't expect me to like him, or him to like me.' She stood up, putting a hand on her brother's shoulder. 'I hope you'll be happy. It will be something of a novelty in our family if you are!'

Dennis winced. 'Leonor is quite different from our revered mother!' he said sharply.

Camilla's shoulders sagged. 'I'm sure she is,' she said wistfully. 'I wish I were!'

'You look like her,' Dennis said firmly, 'but any further resemblance is entirely coincidental. You couldn't love colour as you do if you were really like her.'

'Couldn't I?' Camilla said bitterly. 'Fashion is as fickle in its way as she ever was!'

'She was shallow—'

'She was cold-hearted,' Camilla retorted. She sighed. 'So am I! I can't even like the thought of having to do with a perfectly ordinary little boy for a few weeks! I envy you, Dennis—it's horrid of me, but I do! I know lots of men, don't I? But I've never cared a rap for any of them. So you see—'

'Only because you've never allowed yourself to,' Dennis interrupted her loyally.

'But I don't want to!'

'One day you will,' he chuckled. 'I didn't want to either, and look what happened to me!'

Camilla laughed with him. She watched her brother as he walked away from her, down the long corridor to his own office. She wished she hadn't agreed to go to Portugal. She was safe in her own office, doing the work she loved. Safe, even from her own thoughts. It was a long time, for instance, since she had last thought of either of their parents. Her father she could only just remember. Her mother she could remember only too well. She and Dennis had traipsed after her all through their childhood, from one city to another, seeking the sun and fresh sensations, going from one temporary relationship to another, in all of which their part had been to keep out of the way, until she had grown up and had blossomed into a beauty that had rivalled and had finally outshone her mother's. It was at that moment that she and Dennis had been sent back to London and told to get on with their own lives. Camilla had been just seventeen, her brother two years older.

That had been eight years ago. Since then Camilla Enterprises had been born and had flourished. Camilla had been mildly astonished and then pathetically grateful to discover that designs that she had doodled with for her own amusement had caught on like wildfire and that she and her brother were financially independent of their mother at last. She had a flair for design, and Dennis was a first-rate salesman. They had made an almost perfect combination, and Camilla Enterprises was now almost as famous as Mary Quant.

Then Dennis had gone on holiday to Portugal. Their mother had been living in Lisbon and if he had visited her, he had said nothing to Camilla about their meeting. But he had stayed on in Lisbon for another week, and had met and fallen in love with Leonor. Things, Camilla thought hopelessly, would never be the same again. A married Dennis was bound to be different from the brother she had always known. It would put the final touch to her loneliness—the loneliness that she wouldn't admit to, except sometimes to herself. But one had to put a good

8

face on these things, and she would go to Portugal and she would dance at his wedding. She would even take charge of Luis while he had his honeymoon, but she wouldn't *like* it! She hadn't gone yet, but already she couldn't wait to get home!

It was early November, the time when Camilla began to think about summer. Dennis had convinced her that she could work on her designs equally well in Portugal, sending them home in batches to be turned into fabrics and stylish clothes by the small army of people who now worked for them.

'It will be good for you,' he had said frankly. 'New places can't fail to give one new ideas.'

'I hate travelling!' she had flashed back.

'Mother has moved on,' Dennis had said dryly.

'Mother has nothing to do with it!'

'Not half! You'll love Portugal!'

Camilla had not believed him. And she didn't now as the plane circled over the city, the sunshine catching on its silver wings. The Tagus curled round the edge of the buildings and the sight of the famous Belem Tower brought an unfamiliar feeling of excitement. Perhaps Dennis had been right after all. Perhaps she might even enjoy her time in Portugal.

The plane came down with a sudden rush and a few minutes later they were trooping out of the cabin into the bright sunshine. A couple of airport buses transferred them to the airport buildings for the brief formalities of passport control and Customs and then they were free to go out into the city.

Dennis had travelled out on an earlier flight and he was there to meet her now, accompanied by a plump, radiant woman who was obviously Leonor. Camilla eyed her curiously, remarking the way her hem hung unevenly at an unfashionable length and the shapeless

9

cardigan that hung over her shoulders. And yet, Camilla was forced to admit, Leonor triumphantly surmounted the disadvantage of her clothes. She drew all eyes to her, superbly confident in her own womanhood and attraction. She was gay and vivid and more full of life than anyone Camilla had ever met. No wonder Dennis had been bowled over at first sight of her.

Leonor flashed her a smile. 'I 'ave 'eard so much,' she claimed gaily, 'and now I see it is all true!'

A little shaken, Camilla forced a smile. She felt tall and ice-cold by comparison with her future sister-in-law.

'How do you do?' she said briefly.

'I am well,' Leonor assured her with satisfaction. 'I am very well! Luis and I 'ave been longing to meet you, and now you are finally here! Let us hurry 'ome and make the most of today. It is such a shame that tomorrow Dennis and I go away already, but we shall know each other well by then!'

Camilla hoped not. She didn't like being rushed by anyone into a friendship that might or might not mean anything to her.

'Where is your son?' she asked coolly.

'Luis? 'e is at home. It is kind of you to see to him while I am away. But 'e is very good—no trouble to anyone!'

Camilla looked concerned. 'But should he be left on his own?' she began.

Leonor laughed, attracting every eye to her gay face. 'It is Luis who looks after me, rather than I looking after him. He is serious like his father.'

'He—he can't be very old,' Camilla objected.

'Nine years old,' Leonor said, smiling.

Camilla smiled too. 'Dennis says he's very like you—'

Leonor chuckled. 'In looks,' she admitted. 'But his

ways are his father's. There is no doubt that he is a Ferrado, even if they don't care to admit it. Poor lad, a lord for his father and a fishwife for his mother!'

Dennis was the only one who laughed. 'Quite a mixture!'

'Was his father really a lord?' Camilla asked.

Dennis shook his head. 'But aristocratic!' he said significantly. 'The family are huge landowners, but Luis's father was the younger son. His brother inherited everything, not that they bothered to tell Leonor, but it was all in the papers. Luis's grandfather died quite recently.'

'May he rest in peace,' Leonor added piously, the twinkle in her eye very pronounced. 'He never *lived* in peace with anyone!' she added maliciously. 'Come on, Dennis, let us go. Your sister will be wanting to see down town Lisbon. Me, I live in the part that survived the earthquake, the Alfama—'

'You wait until you see it!' Dennis enthused. 'The streets are fantastically narrow—if you can call them streets; they're more like staircases going up between the old Moorish houses. The name Alfama is from the Arabic.'

'When was the earthquake?' Camilla asked carelessly.

Leonor looked at her in astonishment. 'Don't you know anything about us?' she asked, sounding in some way hurt.

Camilla was immediately embarrassed. 'I don't think we ever came to Portugal,' she said sharply.

'No,' Dennis agreed. 'The nearest was Madrid.'

'But that is not at all the same!' Leonor averred warmly. 'Portugal is your oldest ally. Did you not know that? Spain is your traditional enemy until quite recently.'

Dennis looked amused. 'You get used to it,' he said to his sister. 'Here in Portugal, it's difficult to believe that Henry the Navigator didn't set out on his travels yesterday!'

Leonor flounced towards the nearest door. 'He too was half English!' she said with a spurt of temper.

Camilla looked merely confused.

'Ignoramus!' Dennis teased her. '*Everyone* knows that his mother was Philippa of Lancaster.'

'D-do they?' Camilla said, trying not to laugh.

'Of course they do!' he returned calmly. 'And *her* father was John of Gaunt.'

'G-goodness! That was a long time ago!' Camilla muttered.

'I told you!' Leonor insisted with passion. 'We are your oldest allies. And not only then!'

'No, there was Catherine of Braganza, poor lady,' Dennis went on, his tongue in his cheek.

Camilla remembered with something like relief that Catherine had been the consort of Charles II. She was not much good at this sort of game because her education had been sadly neglected.

'I think I might have liked to have been married to the Merry Monarch,' she said.

Leonor gave her a shocked look. 'He was a bad family man,' she said with finality.

'Does that matter?' Camilla drawled indifferently.

'To me it does!' Leonor declared fiercely. 'If the family doesn't matter to a man, nothing does!'

Camilla and Dennis exchanged glances. 'I hope you heard that,' Camilla remarked in his ear. 'She means it.'

Dennis shrugged. 'I know. It's like a breath of fresh air to me. It gives me a warm feeling of security that you and I never had before.'

Camilla pulled a face at him. 'I prefer to feel completely independent,' she said.

'That's what I thought,' Dennis answered in such

superior tones that she felt like kicking him. ' I've learned better now.'

Camilla lifted her chin. ' I shall never depend on *anyone*!' she claimed. ' I prefer to walk alone.'

Dennis merely grinned. ' I thought that too,' he said.

They emerged out of the airport buildings into the sunshine. It was as warm as an English summer's day, with a light breeze just moving the dust in the corners of the forecourt. Leonor led the way towards a Mini-Morris and pulled open the door for Dennis to climb into the back. She held the door for Camilla to get into the front passenger seat and then hurtled round the bonnet, flinging herself into the driving seat.

' I hope you have the good nerves,' she smiled at Camilla. ' In Lisbon we play a game between the traffic and the pedestrians. Sometimes one side wins, sometimes the other.'

The car roared out into the street, making Camilla wince. But the traffic was not as bad as she had been made to believe. Leonor drove well and she knew exactly where she was going, talking and pointing out the sights as they went.

' This is the new part of the town,' she explained. ' The roads are all messy because we are extending the Metro system out here. It will be good when it is completed.' She went on to point out the ruined castle of St George that dominated the city. ' We are nearly there now.'

She stopped the car by a large and modern statue of St Vincent and hurried them out.

' Take Camilla to the house,' she ordered Dennis, ' while I put the car away.'

Dennis nodded agreeably. He crossed the road and began descending the steps that led down between the box-like houses. At one point, he turned to the left and pushed his way through the fish-market. Gleaming silver fish of all types, huge prawns from the Tagus, crayfish and lobsters jostled against each other on the narrow table. The fishwives called their wares in strident tones, and the housewives of Lisbon bargained for the best of the catch. Camilla could hardly tear herself away from the colourful sight, but becoming aware that Dennis was almost out of sight, she wriggled her way through the crowd to find him waiting for her at the other end of the passageway.

'It's down these steps,' he said, amused by her interest in her surroundings. 'I told you you'd get plenty of ideas if you came to Lisbon,' he added.

'You were right,' Camilla said generously. 'Just look at those rainbow colours on those fish!'

He laughed. 'Good enough to eat!'

'I suppose so,' she smiled, for she had not been considering them as food at all. 'Fancy living in such a place!'

'You will be for the next few weeks,' he reminded her.

'I shall love it!' she exclaimed.

He jumped down the last of the steps and pushed open a heavy wooden door. 'Welcome to Leonor's home!' he bowed.

She stepped through the door and was surprised to find the house much bigger than she had imagined. All the houses clung to one another like the pieces of a jigsaw puzzle, making the rooms uneven in size, depending on which floor they happened to be. In front of the door she could glimpse a small patio, in which a caged canary was singing, and a room which was obviously the kitchen. Dennis gave her a push down a further four stairs and she came into a small sitting room, full of cheap wooden chairs and an antique sideboard of such age and beauty that she could only wonder how they had ever managed to get it through the narrow doors.

'Senhorita Camilla?'

She turned on her heel and met the unblinking stare of a young boy.

'Yes. Are you Luis?'

The boy frowned. 'I am Luis Ferrado.'

Camilla shook hands with him, seeing that it was expected of her. She wondered how Dennis could have thought that the child looked like his mother. Leonor had the strong features and the glowing love of life of her Moorish ancestors. The boy had something more. He had the small hands and feet of the aristocrat and his face already bore the marks of pride, with flaring nostrils and heavy, hooded lids that half-hid his dark eyes.

'I am Camilla Armstrong.'

The boy smiled unexpectedly. 'But you don't have a strong arm,' he objected. 'Dennis has one.'

Camilla bit her lip thoughtfully. 'It was my ancestor who had the strong arm,' she told him. 'He held his shield over the king in a battle, and the king's life was saved. The king himself gave him the name of Armstrong!'

'The king of England?' Luis asked.

Camilla shook her head. 'The king of Scotland.'

'But they are the same,' the boy said disparagingly.

'Not then,' she retorted calmly. 'Then they were enemies, as they were for many centuries.'

'Dennis did not tell me this!' Luis chuckled. 'He said he didn't know anything about his father—just as I don't know mine because he is dead.'

'No,' Camilla admitted with a sigh, 'we don't know anything much about him. Armstrong is a very old name.'

'So is Ferrado!' Luis said quickly, not to be outdone. 'We own land all over Portugal!'

'Now that is enough of that,' Leonor told her son, coming into the room at that moment. 'We do not own

15

any of the land and so it is of no interest to us!'

'But Tio Manoel says—'

'I don't wish to hear! Come on, Luis, we have much to do if your mother is going to marry in the morning. I shall need your help.'

Luis smiled slowly. '*Sim*, Mama,' he agreed.


The wedding was the most exhausting event that Camilla could ever remember. Her own part in the proceedings was small enough. She accompanied the couple to the church and stood awkwardly by Leonor's side, while the Portuguese woman exchanged her vows with Dennis. Leonor was dressed in the most sombre black, which Camilla thought completely unsuitable for any bride, but she managed to look radiantly happy all the same, and the expression of tender love on Dennis's face was reward enough for anyone.

'You disapprove of me?' Leonor said to Camilla on the way home up the steps.

'I don't!' Camilla denied quickly, too quickly. 'But did you have to wear black?'

'I am a widow,' Leonor reminded her.

'But *black*!'

'In Portugal, it is very seldom that a widow will marry again,' Leonor said simply. 'It is not looked upon with favour. But Dennis, he is very persuasive. He says that in England no one will care. Is that true?'

Camilla nodded breathlessly. Climbing up and down the steps in the Alfama district was an art one acquired gradually and she was not yet in practice.

'I shall love England!' Leonor said certainly. 'But Luis will not. He will pine for his native land. I have written to Manoel—' She broke off as Dennis caught up with her and linked her hand in his, smiling up at him. 'Dennis, you will not mind my singing at my own wedding?'

'My personal *fadista*?' he teased her.

She nodded happily. 'It will all be for you!' she agreed.

'Then sing as much as you like!' he said.

It seemed to Camilla that the whole of Lisbon was pressed into the tiny house for the reception, and, as none of them were particularly quiet, the noise was much, much worse than even the public made during one of the rare sales Camilla and Dennis held at their small boutique. Camilla placed herself at a strategic point between the sideboard and the door and wished she had taken the trouble, as her brother had advised, to learn a few words of the sibilant, incomprehensible language that flowed about her.

'Perhaps I can get you something to drink?' a masculine voice asked from somewhere behind her. His accent was so slight that for a moment she thought he was English. She turned her head and smiled at him, the smile turning slowly into astonished bewilderment. The man looked so like Luis as to be ridiculous, only with him the pride in his face had matured into superb self-confidence, a confidence that Camilla found peculiarly irritating. She had met it before in the course of her business life, always from men who had begun by patronising her and had ended by trying to do her down because she was a woman in business.

'Thank you,' she said coldly.

He looked at her for a long moment until she could feel the colour sliding up her cheeks.

'I said I would like a drink,' she reminded him uncomfortably.

He looked amused. He reached over to the sideboard beside her and picked up a glass of wine, handing it to her with a mocking gesture.

'I thought you must be English,' he said. 'A friend

of Dennis Armstrong's?'

She sipped the wine, her eyes lowered. 'Are you?' she countered.

'I've never met him,' the man confessed. 'I came today to see Leonor, but this hardly seems to be a good moment, does it?'

'No,' Camilla agreed.

The man came and stood beside her. His eyes wandered over the crowd and came to rest on Leonor's excited face. Camilla, watching him, saw the disapproval with which he looked at her.

'She's more warm and alive than anyone I've ever met!' she defended her new sister-in-law edgily.

'It is rare in this country for a widow to marry again,' the man remarked.

'Does the same custom apply to widowers?' she asked nastily.

'I believe not.'

She cast him a mocking glance, meeting his eyes squarely. 'How nice for the men!' she drawled.

'That is not the reason,' he answered quietly. 'A woman has the children in her charge. They must be brought up as their father's children, not as the stepchildren of some stranger!'

Camilla shrugged. 'Really? What about Luis? *His* father's family couldn't care less about him!'

'You are an authority on his family?' the man asked quietly.

'They won't even look after him while Dennis and Leonor go on honeymoon!' Camilla snapped.

The hooded eyes lifted to give her a glimpse of the angry eyes beneath. 'Perhaps no one thought to tell them about the approaching wedding?' he murmured.

'Why should they? They didn't go to the *first* wedding!'

The man stood beside her in a rigid silence. Camilla

began to wonder if she had done Leonor a service by provoking him. The expression on his face was one of fury and she couldn't help feeling that he would make someone suffer for the humiliation she had brought him by presenting him with what was no more than the truth.

' You should not speak about things you know nothing about!' he said at last.

' But I do know about it!' Camilla protested. ' Dennis is my brother, so naturally I know all about Leonor.'

' Then you will know that I attended the first wedding,' he retorted smoothly.

' D-did you?' Camilla felt decidedly uncomfortable. ' Are you a member of the family?'

He gave her a wintry smile. ' I think that was clear to you from the beginning,' he said.

Camilla blushed. ' You look very like Luis,' she admitted.

' However,' he went on, ' I should not have come to this wedding without an invitation, had I not received a letter from Leonor—'

' But Leonor would never write to a Ferrado!'

' *Senhorita*, are you always so silly?'

Camilla glared at him. ' You've always been unkind to her!' she insisted.

' My father did not approve the marriage—not that it is any busines of yours!' the man admitted. ' But he did not disinherit Jaime, or his son. Perhaps Leonor did not tell you this?'

Camilla licked her lips. ' No,' she admitted. ' But Leonor's husband was the younger son, wasn't he?'

The man bowed slightly. ' That is correct. His portion of the estate is not vast, but nevertheless Luis will be a reasonably wealthy young man. I have no doubt this Dennis Armstrong was aware of that.'

'No! He didn't know!'

'And how do you know that? By jumping to conclusions again?'

Camilla shook her head. 'I'm Camilla Armstrong,'
she said almost humbly. 'Dennis's sister.'

His eyes returned to her face for a brief moment.
'Then you will be able to present me to your brother?'

'Yes,' she agreed.

'Tell me about him,' he commanded easily. 'What
does he do for a living?'

'He works for me—in a way—' Camilla began. She
stopped abruptly when she saw his lip curl in contempt.

'He works for *you*? But it is he who should provide
for his sister!'

'Isn't that rather old-fashioned?' Camilla asked
coldly.

The man stared at her, the hooded lids almost hiding
his eyes. Camilla felt both distressed and indignant, a
long way from her usual cool assurance, but she wouldn't
give him the satisfaction of dropping her own eyes first.

'Tio Manoel! Tio Manoel! What are you doing
here? Did you come to see me?'

Luis hurled himself across the room and into his
uncle's arms and the man's expression softened immediately at the sight of him. 'Oh, Tio, I am so pleased to
see you!'


CHAPTER II


'Manoel was kind to me when Jaime and I fell in love,'
Leonor maintained, pleating her black skirt between
nervous fingers. 'It was his father who would not
receive me.'

'You never told me that!' Dennis said angrily.

'I did not think you would understand,' Leonor said

20

simply. 'And now you can see that I am quite right!'

'I can't see Manoel being kind to anyone,' Camilla put in with an involuntary shiver. 'He doesn't look kind.'

'Nevertheless he was,' Leonor insisted.

'By coming to the wedding?' Dennis said nastily.

'He came,' Leonor agreed. 'He did not approve of Jaime marrying me, of course. He would have preferred some other arrangement—'

'Like what?' Camilla asked faintly.

'He would have preferred Jaime to have made me his mistress,' Leonor said with simple dignity. 'It is commonplace. The children are looked after by the man's family and her name is protected as far as possible. Manoel offered me a position in his own house!'

Dennis clenched his fists. 'What as?' he demanded.

Leonor looked puzzled for a moment. 'As a maid, of course. There is nothing else I can do.'

'And then, I suppose, later on, Jaime would have made the grand marriage that was expected of him?' Dennis went on.

Leonor nodded. 'It is often like that,' she whispered.

'Not in England, it's not!' Dennis retorted. 'Who does the fellow think he is? He'd better not make any more such suggestions—'

Leonor blinked. She was very near to tears. 'He wants to take Luis home with him while we're away.'

'Over my dead body!' Camilla exclaimed.

'You are to go too,' Leonor explained uneasily.

'No! That's too much! I thought him absolutely hateful! If you want Luis to go with him, that's quite all right with me. I shall go back to England.'

'But I don't want him to go alone,' Leonor protested. 'He is an ordinary little boy and I do not want him to be spoilt and made to feel that he is important. Manoel says he is the Ferrado heir, until Manoel himself marries and has children, and that he must learn what this means—'

'Perhaps he should,' Dennis said thoughtfully.

'And become as unfeeling as his uncle!' Camilla said fiercely. 'I suppose you will applaud when he starts to exercise the *droit de seigneur* and all the other medieval activities of the Ferrado family!'

'And what are those?' Manoel Ferrado asked her smoothly from the doorway. 'You have me intrigued!'

'I should have thought what you suggested for Leonor was bad enough!' she retorted.

'Something else you know nothing about?' he enquired.

'She's just been telling us!' Camilla said flatly.

'They do not understand how kind you were,' Leonor said uneasily. She smiled suddenly, humour lighting up her face. 'English people are very strange. They find it quite normal for someone like Jaime to marry a fishwife like me!'

'That isn't so strange,' Manoel protested.

'That is not what you said at the time!' she laughed.

Manoel smiled. 'At the time it was better that you didn't know what I thought,' he murmured. 'It seemed better to do all that was possible to avoid a family quarrel. My father was not at all well even then. But I think I was quite jealous of Jaime. You are a very beautiful woman, Leonor.'

'You forget that she is now married to me!' Dennis said belligerently.

'I forget nothing,' Manoel returned easily.

'*And* that Luis is now my responsibility!' Dennis added.

'Luis is a Ferrado. As such he is my responsibility, for I am the head of the family.' Manoel turned his back on both Dennis and Camilla, smiling at his sister-in-law. 'You were right to write to me. Luis will home home with me while you are on honeymoon. The Senhorita Camilla will accompany him—'

' I will not!' Camilla flared at him.

The slight shrug with which he greeted her remark irritated her even more. She supposed it was because he didn't care whether she were there or not!

' When did Leonor write to you?' Dennis demanded, gritting his teeth.

' As soon as she knew she was going to marry you,' Manoel returned imperturbably. ' Unfortunately, I did not get her letter immediately because I have been away.'

' It was right that he should know, Dennis,' Leonor said, her eyes pleading with her new husband.

' I don't see that it's any of his confounded business!' Denis said gruffly.

' But it is! He has Luis's future to consider—'

Dennis spread his hands before him, silently demanding reason to come to his aid. ' Luis is nothing to him!'

' That is where you are wrong. I think it would be better if you and your sister returned to the other guests while Leonor and I finish our business discussion. We will tell you what we have decided in a few minutes.'

To Camilla's shame, Dennis showed signs of falling in with this tiresome, proud man's instructions, but nothing would have induced her to leave Leonor alone to face him on her own. She sat down quickly on the nearest spindly chair and glared at him across the room. If they had been wise, she thought, they would not have allowed him to separate them from the party just because he had wished it. Once Leonor and Dennis had departed, he could hardly have prised Luis and herself out of Leonor's house!

' *Senhorita?*' Manoel's amused glance swept over her. ' Perhaps you wish to continue your instruction on how the Ferrados should conduct their affairs?'

23

Camilla blushed, completely forgetting the lesson she had long ago learned in dealing with recalcitrant clients, that it was better to be cool and witty, come what may, than to allow anything to get one into an emotional state.

'I should think there is room for anyone to instruct you in quite a few things!' she retorted sharply. 'Manners, for example!'

'But not by you,' Manoel said certainly.

'Me, or anyone else!' Camilla shrugged.

He laughed shortly. 'I think you would be better employed in packing your bag, *senhorita*. I have every intention of taking Luis home with me and you will not be able to stay on in this house for the next few weeks—'

'Why not?' she shot at him. 'It's Leonor's house!'

'I am afraid it is my house,' he said quietly. 'I have no wish to have you stay here. Is that enough for you?'

Leonor took an impulsive step forward. 'It was bought from my father as somewhere for Jaime and me to live,' she told Camilla apologetically. 'Manoel bought it for us.'

'I thought he took no interest in you after Jaime died?' Dennis said witheringly to his wife.

'My *father* took no interest,' Manoel amended.

'Well then?' Dennis prompted him.

'I am not my father,' Manoel said in amused tones. 'Naturally I saw it as my duty to provide for my brother's son and heir. I shall continue to do this. Luis will spend half his time with me and half his time with his mother. That is what I have decided.'

'Thank you, Manoel,' Leonor said meekly.

'*Thank you!*' Camilla repeated in scorn. 'What for? For taking Luis away from you for most of the time?'

'*Senhorita!*'

Camilla drew herself up. '*Dennis* will provide for both Leonor and Luis in the future!'

'Meaning that you will? I am sorry, *senhorita*, but

24

I do not like to think of any Ferrado having to depend on your generosity!'

'And just what do you mean by that?' she asked him dangerously.

'I mean that you may marry, *senhorita*. What will happen to your business then?'

'I shall never marry!' she declared.

'Never?' His eyes lingered on her piled-up fair hair and the line of her cheek. 'But I understood your business is very successful? Someone is sure to marry you for your money even if they can find no other attraction, don't you think?'

'I meant that *I* will never marry anyone,' Camilla answered sweetly. 'Not even a fortune-hunter! Though I fancy that I could marry *and* work, being English and independent and not one of the Ferrado dependents—or whatever you call the people whose destiny you obviously enjoy controlling!'

Manoel Ferrado laughed harshly. 'You are so sure about everything!' he mocked her. 'I think the evidence will prove you wrong again,' he added.

'*Never!*'

He laughed again. 'Be that as it may, I do not choose to have a member of my family dependent on you—'

'I don't care what you decide about Luis,' she informed him loftily. 'But I make my own decisions, *senhor*. I shall go back to England on the first available flight.'

Dennis took a quick, audible breath. 'But you can't!' he protested.

Camilla turned to him immediately. 'Why not?'

Her brother looked uncomfortable. 'Come over here,' he begged. 'I've got to speak to you.'

Nearer the door they could hear the noise of the party still going on. What a wedding! Camilla felt suddenly poignantly sorry for her brother.

'What is it?' she whispered to him.

'Just about everything has gone wrong, hasn't it?' he said bitterly. 'But it isn't Leonor's fault. I don't want the whole day ruined for her. She has this hang-up over the Ferrados, though God knows why she should feel under any obligation to them!'

'No,' Camilla said briefly.

'If Jaime was anything like this one though I might be able to understand it,' Dennis went on wryly.

Camilla screwed up her face with distaste. 'Too obvious!' she observed dryly.

Dennis actually laughed. 'He hasn't been exactly subtle,' he admitted. 'I wonder why he dislikes you so much?'

'That's easily answered,' Camilla said, superbly confident in her own judgement. 'He's so used to boss-ing women about, he doesn't like to know that there's even one who can afford to cock a snook at him! I certainly don't care who he is, or how much money he's got!'

Dennis looked startled. 'But you're not very cool about him, are you?'

'Of course I am!' Camilla forced a laugh. 'You know I never allow anyone to affect me deeply. We both ought to know better than that!'

'It isn't always something one can control,' Dennis pointed out.

Camilla blinked. 'I've never been tempted,' she admitted. She had a horrid feeling that Dennis was already regretting his involvement with Leonor. Love them and leave them had been her mother's motto. Surely it could never creep into yet another generation in Dennis?

'Leonor has been brought up to submit to people like Manoel Ferrado,' she said quickly.

'Don't I know it!'

26

' Then be patient, Dennis.'

' I'm trying to be. But *I'm* her husband now, not Jaime Ferrado. Sooner or later she'll have to choose which of us she wants.'

Camilla sighed. ' She said it wasn't the custom for Portuguese widows to remarry,' she reminded him sadly.

' Do you think I don't know that?' He looked decidedly harassed and more than a little inadequate. Camilla was annoyed to find herself thinking that he was no match for Manoel.

' What are you going to do?' she asked him.

' Go on with the honeymoon,' he said dully. ' I can't stop that man taking Luis home with him, especially if Leonor says he can go, but I don't want him to have everything his own way. That's what I'm going to ask you, Cam. He says you can go with Luis. I know you won't like it, but I need someone to look after my interests.' He smiled briefly. ' I usually look after yours,' he added carefully. ' You're not expected home for a while. Don't you think you could give it a go?'

' But what could I do?' Camilla objected.

' I don't know,' he admitted. ' You'll think of something! Make him see that he has no right to come between a man and his wife—'

Camilla giggled. ' He's never seen anything he didn't want to!'

' Nor do you!' Dennis said flatly.

' I do!' Camilla protested. ' I'm not deliberately unkind to anyone anyway. I think he could be.'

' He won't do you any harm in a few weeks,' Dennis dismissed this. ' Please, Camilla, go with Luis. I don't want to lose Leonor, or any part of her, and I will if he takes Luis away from her.'

This was no more than the truth. Camilla glanced across the room to where Manoel Ferrado was standing. Why not? she thought. It might even be fun to upset a few of his carefully complacent plans. How he would hate it! Her eyes gleamed at the thought. She would look after Dennis's interests with a vengeance, she thought, and because she was uninvolved and had something of her mother in her, she would even enjoy it!

Most of the wedding guests had gone, but a few still lingered. Camilla was surprised to discover that there were still some unopened bottles of wine on the antique sideboard and a little intrigued to read the legend *Casa Ferrado* emblazoned on their labels.

' I brought them with me,' Manoel told her. ' Have you tasted our wine yet?'

Camilla confessed that she hadn't. He opened one of the bottles, his strong, tanned hands showed to advantage while he dealt with the cork and poured the semi-sparkling *vinho verde* into a tulip-shaped glass.

' Try it,' he said. ' This is one of the famous Portuguese green wines. It means that the grapes are picked when they are still green. It has nothing to do with the colour of the wine.'

' Oh,' Camilla said inadequately. She took a cautious sip, determined to find it inferior because it was Portuguese and *his*, and not French or Spanish. But she found it completely delicious, with a strong taste of grapes and a clear, strong bouquet.

' Well?' Manoel prompted her.

' Do you make any other wines?' she asked him.

He looked amused, noting the fact that she hadn't answered him. ' We grow five different varieties of vine on the different estates. This is my favourite.'

' The green wine? Why don't they grow it in—Spain?'

Manoel's eyes glinted with sudden humour. ' I've never thought about it. Perhaps when we divided the world between us, we agreed on different methods of viticulture too.'

Camilla lifted her chin crossly. 'You were a bit previous in your division of the world, weren't you? You reckoned without the British!'

He watched her lazily. 'You were no more than irritating pirates at the time. I believe you drank beer and mead—'

'While you robbed and cheated people all round the world!' Camilla interrupted him.

His eyebrows rose dramatically. 'More ill-formed opinions? You are thinking of the Spanish Conquistadores, no doubt?'

Camilla bit her lip. 'Did the Portuguese behave so well, then?' she demanded.

'According to their lights,' he answered. 'We are proud of Vasco da Gama, as you are of your great explorers.'

'I suppose so,' she said, suddenly tired of sparring with him. It was foolish to argue about something she knew nothing about. One day, she thought, she would choose the subject and then he could watch out! She would flay him alive!

One of the wedding guests slipped into the centre of the room and the man who was with her began to strum on a stringed instrument that looked like an old-fashioned dulcimer. Suddenly the woman threw back her head and began to sing. There was an immediate silence while the sad sound of her song filled the room. She ended as suddenly as she had begun, on a full unstrained note, as harsh as a shout and as true as any opera note.

'That is the typical sound of Lisbon,' Manoel told Camilla. 'You will not like our *fado*.'

'It's a sad sound,' Camilla said.

'Of course. It is a song of fate, with just that touch of *saudade*—it is not quite sadness—that is a part of our

29

national character.'

Camilla watched the singer accept a glass of wine and join her friends again, calmly accepting their compliments. Several times Leonor's name was mentioned, but there was no sign of her sister-in-law. She and Dennis were still talking in the bedroom.

'Leonor will sing before she goes,' Manoel interrupted her thoughts with a slight smile.

'At her own wedding?' Camilla drawled.

He shrugged. 'It is an audience,' he said indifferently.

Camilla stared at him with disapproval. 'There's no need for you to make your contempt for anyone who is not a Ferrado so obvious!' she told him sharply.

There was no mistaking the anger in his eyes. 'It is you who approves and disapproves of others. I accept Leonor as she is, but that is a different matter altogether.'

'Naturally!'

He looked at her for a long moment, his eyes thoughtful. 'There was another Armstrong in Lisbon a few weeks ago,' he said suddenly. 'I had the pleasure of meeting her on one occasion. You have a strong look of her—'

Camilla felt her muscles stiffen. 'You must mean my mother,' she said.

She had the satisfaction of seeing Manoel put out of countenance, but it wasn't much of a victory, for she thought she knew exactly what he thought of all the Armstrongs now. She threw back her head, determined not to let him see that she cared a jot what he thought about any of them.

'Perhaps it wasn't my mother after all,' she went on. 'Few handsome men emerge unscathed from meeting her.'

'Is she so fierce?'

Camilla laughed lightly. 'Fierce, *senhor*? No, I wouldn't call her fierce at all. On the contrary, she is beautiful and yielding—'

'Very unlike her daughter!'

'Exactly,' Camilla agreed thankfully. 'If there is any resemblance between us, it's just a surface, physical thing.'

Manoel watched her closely. 'It is interesting to know that you think me handsome,' he said at last. 'I can return the compliment. You are a lovely-to-look-at woman, *senhorita*, as fair as you are cold.'

Camilla coloured slightly. 'I meant that my mother would find you handsome!' she said rudely.

'That was understood,' he drawled. 'You are too untouched by your surroundings to notice anyone else's looks.'

'That isn't true!' she protested.

'No?' he taunted her.

'You know you are good-looking,' she accused him.

'But not attractive to you?'

'Certainly not!'

He looked amused. 'Nor you to me,' he said.

Camilla swallowed the last of her wine, more embarrassed than she would admit. No one else had ever spoken to her in such terms! The men she knew treated her as an equal and they spoke about their business interests together, not whether they held any attraction for each other!

'Why not?' she said before she had thought.

'I like warmth and generosity in my women,' he answered her. He turned and saw his sister-in-law coming into the room. 'Ah,' he murmured, 'she comes to sing to us as I promised you!' His eyes met Camilla's again fleetingly. 'She makes an interesting contrast to your English ice. She has all the impulsive fire that a man could wish for—'

'I think she's lovely!' Camilla agreed gravely.

'Wait until you've heard her sing,' he answered softly.

' That is the moment of truth!'

Leonor did not need pressing very hard to sing. She raised her shawl over her head, her face strangely pale against the black of her clothes.

' I shall sing this in English, for my husband,' she announced, a faint catch in her voice. ' For Dennis,' she added, lest there should be any misunderstanding on the point.

The silence in the room grew into something that was almost tangible. Leonor's eyes flickered over their expectant faces, choosing her moment with the effortless ease of the born performer. When she began to sing, the street-crier quality of her voice echoed piercingly in Camilla's ears. She wasn't sure that she wanted to listen to such a heartbreaking sound, but she couldn't help herself. The sound echoed her own heart-beat, making her flesh tingle with a strange, previously unknown excitement.

' This is by João Zorro, from the thirteenth century,' Leonor announced abruptly. She stood with her feet slightly apart and with her bosom pushed out in front of her, her head held high.

> *Below, where the river meets the sea,*
> *I and love will go*
> *Where the king arms his ship*
> *Love, I will go with you.'*

The notes died away and Camilla felt strangely near to tears. There was so much love in Leonor's voice that Dennis had no excuse for not knowing how she felt about him. Camilla almost envied him, it was so different from that fickle, amusing emotion that their mother called love.

Manoel held a finger at the corner of her eye and caught a tear before she could brush it away and pretend herself unmoved.

' It doesn't mean a thing!' Camilla assured him

crossly.

'It is Portugal pulling at your heartstrings,' he teased her gently.

'No,' she denied positively. 'It has nothing to do with Portugal!'

He said nothing, but she could tell that he didn't believe her.

'You forget,' she rushed on, 'that I haven't any heartstrings to pull!' she blinked. 'You have to be made of flesh and blood to have such things!'

Amusement tugged at the corner of his mouth. 'Are you issuing me with a challenge?' he asked, so quietly that she had to strain her ears to hear him. 'This is neither the time nor the place, Camilla, but there will be other times.'

'I haven't given you the right to use my name!' she retorted proudly.

'Forgive me, *senhorita*,' he replied. 'It is a name which suits you so well.' His hand encircled her wrist and he tethered her firmly to his side. 'I think your brother and Leonor are now leaving, so we may do so too, if Luis is ready. Where are your cases?'

Camilla chuckled. 'You'd like me to have mountains of luggage so that you could be superior about my feminine extravagance!' she said with spirit. 'I have one suitcase, I'll have you know, and it conforms strictly to the airlines' restrictions, so there!'

He laughed with her. 'I am surprised, yes,' he admitted. 'I thought such elegance would require the support of a large wardrobe!'

She blushed, pleased beyond all measure that he should call her elegant. Then she remembered immediately that it was part of her stock in trade to be elegant, that that was what her business was all about, and she felt suddenly unsure of herself and gauche.

'I design clothes,' she said starkly.

The pressure of his fingers on her wrist increased. 'And Dennis?' he asked.

'He sells the things I design—' She broke off. 'Not that it's any of your business!' she ended.

'None at all,' he agreed smoothly. 'But I am fond enough of Leonor to wish her happy.'

'And—Luis?'

He let her go, moving forward with the rest of the guests to watch Dennis and Leonor as they ran down the steps away from the house to the waiting taxi down at the bottom of the hill.

'Luis *is* my business,' he said.

It was a strange feeling, standing outside Leonor's house, with Luis's warm hand tucked into her own, while Manoel locked the door and picked up her suitcase, leading the way down the steps to the street below. A few young men stood in the square outside the church. Camilla could feel their eyes moving over her in the frank assessment of the opposite sex that all Iberians indulge in. She hurried her footsteps, almost tripping down the last few steps to the street below.

Manoel flicked his fingers to a passing taxi and the green-roofed, black Mercedes came to a violent stop beside them. Luis pulled the door open and clambered in, forcing Camilla to sit between himself and his uncle.

Manoel leaned forward and gave the driver his address. Camilla caught the sound of the Ferrado name and was almost surprised that he found it necessary to say that his house was in the Belem district.

'Where do you live?' she asked him, a new anxiety occurring to her as she realised that she had no idea where she was going.

'Close to the river,' he replied. 'Close too to the Jeronimos Monastery.'

'It is the most beautiful house in Lisbon!' Luis

34

chimed in.

'Spoken like a true Ferrado!' Manoel said dryly. 'I admit to agreeing with him in my own mind. It is a very fine place in which to live.'

Camilla said nothing. The taxi sped along the wide street beside the river, passing the fish market and a railway station, into the Black Horse Square, the nick-name given to the famous Praça do Comercio, where the ferries come and go across the river Tagus. She caught a glimpse of the lit-up Jeronimos Monastery, the monument to the Explorers, and the Tower of Belem, before they hurried up a narrow side street and turned back somehow to the river again, drawing up outside an impressively large house that she wished she could see better in the darkness.

'May I ring the bell? May I, Tio Manoel?' Luis pleaded.

His uncle nodded, feeling in his pocket for the few coins necessary to pay off the taxi.

The ornate front door was flung open, allowing a shaft of light to fall on the black and white mosaic of the pave-ment. Now that she was there, Camilla hung back, reluctant to go inside Manoel's own private domain.

'You can run away tomorrow,' he said in her ear. 'Tonight you have only to eat and sleep. Will that be so awful?'

She shook her head, smiling despite herself at her own foolishness. Then taking a deep breath, she clutched Luis's eager hand in hers and allowed him to drag her over the threshold into the most beautiful hallway she had ever seen.

# CHAPTER III

Camilla had always been very much affected by her surroundings. Perhaps because she was cautious of her relationships with other people, places had become even more important to her. The small flat that she shared with Dennis in London was a delight to her, especially when she thought of the sombre rooms they had taken over in the beginning. She had redecorated the place herself and, because at that time there had been very little money to spare, she had haunted the sales rooms to find just the pieces of furniture she had wanted at a reasonable price.

Now, standing in the hall of Manoel's house, she knew that her highest ambitions had fallen short of what could be achieved. This house was like a dream she had long tried to remember when she was awake and working. It was perfection. The stairs rose in two perfectly balanced curves, meeting in the centre, the banisters so delicately worked that it was hard to believe they had been carved of wood. The walls were hung about with paintings of the Manoeline period, full of such symbols as the belted globe and the cross of the Order of Christ. But, best of all, were the enormous chandeliers that lit a tiled frieze that followed the curve of the stairs, depicting some court scene of the eighteenth century and the members of the Ferrado family at the time, proud and beautifully robed, and all of them looking exactly like Manoel.

Her eyes widened appreciatively and then, seeing Manoel's amusement at her reaction, she blushed.

'It's a beautiful house,' she said defensively.

'I thought you might like it,' he answered, not bothering to hide the fact that he was laughing at her.

Camilla took a step closer to Luis, glad of the small boy's support.

'It's marvellous what money can do,' she said in a light, bored voice that she hoped would annoy the house's owner. It did.

'Very slappable!' he commented briefly.

She looked at him out of the corner of her eye, a little afraid of him. 'It's no more than the truth!'

His eyebrows rose. 'I suppose your parents found the same trait in you rather trying?' he enquired politely.

'Why should they?' Camilla asked blandly.

'I wondered that you should agree so easily that you deserved slapping down,' he said, equally smooth.

Camilla's furious countenance made him laugh out loud. 'I *hate* you!' she informed him breathlessly.

'I doubt it,' he retorted indifferently. 'People agree with you too easily. That's the trouble with women when they have positions of power, it goes to their heads like wine!'

'I don't have a position of power!' she snapped.

'I thought the whole of Camilla Enterprises rested on your shoulders?' he said over his shoulder, dexterously moving her across the hall towards the first of the sitting rooms, the least formal, where the family usually gathered.

'I do most of the designing,' she said sulkily.

His eyes flicked over her. 'And your brother does most of the selling?'

She nodded. The sitting room in its own way was as beautiful as the hall and she was beginning to wish that she had not tried to antagonise her host. It was a privilege to stay in such a beautiful house, no matter what the circumstances. It was an opportunity that could only come once in a lifetime and she didn't really want to spoil it for herself.

'I'm sorry,' she said flatly. 'I know it takes more

than money—'

'But your hackles rise at the sight of me,' he said quite pleasantly. 'I wonder why?'

'Because your whole family has been so unkind to Leonor!'

His eyebrows rose in a quizzical expression. 'Are you always so impulsive?' he asked her gently.

She frowned. 'I wouldn't have said I was impulsive at all!'

'Then it must be your ill nature,' he observed.

'But you *have* been unkind to Leonor,' she persisted.

'If you say so,' he answered with maddening calm.

'Tell me in what way you have been *kind* to her!'

'I think you do not understand our ways,' he said. 'I am trying hard not to fall into the same trap myself. I prefer to think that I have misunderstood you than that you are ill-mannered.'

She gasped. 'I think—I think you're quite odious!' she exclaimed, exasperated.

He crossed the room and rang the bell in the wall. 'I think you would like to see your room immediately?' he suggested. 'My housekeeper, Carlota, will see that you have everything you need.'

Feeling herself dismissed, Camilla followed the black, waiting shadow of the housekeeper up the stairs to a well-appointed bedroom at one end of the landing. An enormous carved four-poster bed dominated the room, matched by the heavy brocade curtains that glinted a reflection to the switched on light.

'*Abrigada*,' she smiled at the housekeeper.

Carlota replied in perfect English. 'I hope you will be comfortable. The *senhor* insisted that you should have this room, though I should have preferred to have put you in one of the simpler rooms upstairs. The *senhor* himself sleeps on this floor.'

Camilla swallowed. 'Why—why this room?' she

asked.

Carlota shrugged. 'Who knows? This room is usually kept for the *senhora* his mother, or the *senhora* his sister. I have never known a guest to be allowed in here.' She stared thoughtfully at Camilla, though not unkindly. ' I have arranged for one of the maids to sleep in here with you,' she added with determination.

' That won't be necessary,' Camilla said hollowly. ' I would sooner move my room.'

' The *senhor*, he said—'

' I don't care what the *senhor* said! I shall speak to him myself!'

Carlota made a last effort. ' The girl will not disturb you in any way,' she said smoothly.

' I'm sorry,' Camilla returned with equal determination. ' I have never shared my bedroom with anyone.' She gave the housekeeper an appealing look. ' Couldn't I sleep upstairs? Where is your room?'

' It is upstairs,' the housekeeper admitted. ' There is nobody on this landing except the *senhor* himself and the *senhor* Luis. He is in the room next to yours.'

Camilla stood up swiftly. ' I'll go and speak to the *senhor* about it now. Whatever happens, though, I will not have anyone else sleeping in my bedroom, and that's that!'

Carlota stood courteously aside as Camilla rushed out of the room and down the stairs again, her head held high as she swept into the sitting room where she had left Manoel. He was seated on a chair, close to the fire that had been recently lit, more for its looks than because any additional warmth was needed. He stood up immediately, looking enquiringly at her.

' It's about my room,' she burst out.

The look on his face brought her to a stumbling halt. She had never encountered such arrogant contempt in anyone.

39

'There is something the matter with your room?' he asked in tones of total disbelief.

'N-no,' she admitted. 'It's a perfectly lovely room, as you very well know!'

'Then I fail to see why we must have a scene about it,' he murmured.

She blenched. 'I don't want to have anyone sleeping in my room!' she protested wretchedly.

To her dismay he laughed. 'You are not in England now!' he told her.

She glared at him. 'I know that! But it's outrageous that some poor girl should have to come and sleep in my room because, for some reason, known only to yourself, you insist that I should sleep on the same floor as yourself!'

'Perhaps I find it convenient,' he suggested mendaciously.

'Don't be ridiculous!' she chided him. 'Why should you?'

He laughed again. 'When you are angry enough you are quite attractive,' he drawled.

She felt winded and more than a little uncertain. 'I don't understand—' she began. Her eyes widened. 'At least, I don't *think* I do!' She gazed at him with a touch of indignation. 'I don't think *you* would ever bother me,' she added, her voice fading away with the shock he had given her.

'But you can't be quite sure, can you?' he said gravely.

She pulled herself together with an effort. 'Of course I can be sure! I'm not your type!'

He looked amused. 'Not when I thought you as cool as your looks, but now I know you can make a scene about nothing, just like any other woman, it might be amusing to find out what lies beneath the exterior—'

'How dare you?' she protested.

He smiled. ' Also,' he went on, ' Luis has never been away from his mother before and he might need you in the night. There is only one vacant room on the second floor.'

' Luis would have you,' she pointed out eagerly.

' I am sure you have a more motherly touch than I,' he murmured.

Camilla felt completely shattered. ' Me?'

' Yes, you. Why not? All woman plan eventually to be mothers, don't they?'

' No, they do not!' She was more flustered than ever. ' I've never even considered it! It's the last thing I want! I'm quite happy as I am!'

He plainly disbelieved her, though he was too polite to say so. More annoyed than she could say, she flounced round to face him.

' I have my work!' she exclaimed.

' And you find that enough?'

' Of course,' she said indignantly.

Her eyes met his briefly and she could feel herself blushing. She looked away hastily, bitterly conscious of the bright amusement in his.

' I think you may have persuaded yourself that that is so,' he said. ' But you lack the courage to put it to the test!'

She stuck out her chin in a belligerent gesture. ' I am not a coward, *senhor*!'

Manoel took a step towards her and she had to clench her fists to make herself hold her ground. She would not retreat! Why should she? She didn't even like him, so what did she have to fear? She had never wanted anything more than her work and a certain amount of companionship from Dennis.

She felt his hands on her shoulders and she shut her eyes.

' It's not too late to run away,' he told her right in

her ear.

But it was. His mouth came down on hers and his hands caressed her, forcing her body close against his. Her lips parted beneath his and she found herself responding to his kiss with a depth of emotion that she had never suspected lay dormant within her.

'You see?' he said, every inch the triumphant male. He pulled her back into his arms and kissed her again until she uttered a small sound of protest.

'I could so easily want you!' he said sharply. 'Perhaps now you understand a little more about our Portuguese customs?'

'But we don't like each other!' She put up a hand and made a feeble effort to capture a loose strand of honey-coloured hair.

'Liking has nothing to do with it,' he told her dryly.

'N-no, I suppose not,' she managed.

'So,' he added firmly, 'we shall have no more complaints about a maid sleeping in your bedroom?'

'No,' she agreed wearily. With an effort she made herself look at him, wondering what it was about him that had made her most deeply held resolutions crumble before his touch.

'Good,' he said.

She recovered herself a little. 'You needn't have made your point quite so ruthlessly,' she said, on the edge of tears.

'No? I think it better that we should understand one another from the start.'

Camilla made another effort to tidy her hair. 'You don't understand me at all!' she told him flatly.

He smiled without amusement. 'I think it is you who do not understand yourself,' he said.

'Oh!' she exclaimed. 'You're quite impossible! What makes you think you're omniscient about everyone and everything? I've never met anyone so arrogant,

He laughed this time with real enjoyment. 'It's time you encountered a man for once in your tidy life!'

She drew herself up with dignity. 'I know several men!'

He laughed again. 'All of whom depend on you for a living, I suppose. They aren't men at all!'

'Why not? There's nothing wrong with working for a woman!'

His eyes glinted with an emotion she couldn't guess at. 'Of course not,' he agreed with sudden charm. 'Not if they are men in their private lives.'

'What do you mean by that?' she flared at him.

'Even if I worked for you, *senhorita*, I should see that you had no chance to interfere in what I did, or did not do!'

Camilla swallowed indignantly. 'I don't interfere in the private lives of any of my employees!' she said angrily.

His eyes challenged her. 'What woman could resist it?' he retorted.

She turned on her heel and walked out of the room. It was silly to let him needle her, she told herself fiercely. He knew nothing about her, or about her business! Was Dennis less of a man because his salary depended on her inspiration? It was a ridiculous supposition! And yet it would be a relief to have someone *she* could rely on, instead of everyone relying on her.

She thought dispassionately about her work and the calm, even life she had made for herself. It was *safe*, and she liked that. She didn't feel safe with Manoel Ferrado. In a few minutes he had given her a glimpse of a perilous excitement that had warmed her whole being. But it was not for her. She knew where such feelings could lead. They led straight to the nomadic,

43

brittle relationships that her mother had enjoyed ever since Camilla could remember.

Dinner—if dinner it could be called—was an uncomfortable meal. Luis was practically asleep and had eaten more than enough at the reception not to want to eat again, and Camilla was so conscious of Manoel sitting at the end of the table that her hands shook as she tried to manipulate her knife and fork.

'What will we do tomorrow, Tio?' Luis asked his uncle.

'What would you like to do?' Manoel drawled, his eyes on Camilla.

Camilla jerked her head upwards. 'I'm sure Luis would prefer to speak Portuguese,' she told him. 'Please don't mind me. I want to learn a few words before I go home anyway.'

Manoel frowned. 'It would not be good manners,' he said abruptly.

Camilla looked down at her plate. 'I had always thought it *good* manners to put the people around one at their ease,' she murmured.

'That comes into it,' Manoel agreed smoothly. 'There are other aspects—like protecting women, if one is a man, and being grateful for male solicitude if one is a woman.'

'I had never heard it called that before,' Camilla answered innocently.

His eyebrows shot up. 'No? What would you call it?'

'Assault and battery,' she responded with feeling.

Luis giggled. 'Tio Manoel doesn't allow people to be rough,' he told her a shade smugly. 'He says a man should never hurt a woman!'

'What a pity he doesn't practise what he preaches!' Camilla commented lightly.

'Why? Did he hurt you?' Luis demanded with

44

interest.

'No, I did not,' Manoel put in. 'Senhorita Camilla was only joking.'

Camilla smiled faintly. 'I never joke about serious matters,' she said.

Luis's interest was well and truly caught. 'What did he do, Camilla?'

'Well, Camilla?' Manoel pressed her.

Camilla stirred uncomfortably. 'I thought we were talking about good manners,' she reminded them. 'I don't believe any Ferrado has any manners!'

Manoel hooted with laughter. 'Because we ask you a question?'

'That you know the answer to!' she snapped back.

Luis looked from one to the other. 'Did you hurt her, Tio Manoel?'

'I kissed her,' his uncle told him.

Luis looked disgusted. 'Kissing doesn't hurt!' he protested to Camilla.

'Nor is it good manners when the lady doesn't wish to be kissed,' she said firmly.

Luis nodded knowingly. 'People sometimes want to kiss me,' he sighed. 'Nasty wet kisses which I *hate!*'

'*Exactly!*' Camilla agreed with a touch of triumph.

'Did he kiss you like that?' Luis asked.

Camilla felt herself blushing. She could feel Manoel's interest in her answer. 'It was a bit like that,' she compromised.

Luis frowned. 'A bit?' he repeated.

'What was the rest like?' Manoel asked, giving every sign of being as fascinated by the conversation as his nephew was.

'It—It—Oh, I hate you!' Camilla exploded.

'Which means she liked it,' Manoel informed Luis with satisfaction.

'It does not!' Camilla denied, exasperated.

45

'Tio Manoel's kisses aren't wet,' Luis added, following his own train of thought to the end. 'Not like Tia Maria's.' His eyes rested reproachfully on Camilla. 'Her kisses are horrid!'

'I don't like being kissed by anyone!' Camilla said stormily.

'Liar!' Manoel muttered *sotto voce*.

She flushed. 'You don't know anything about it!'

His eyes met hers, a gleam of humour in their depth. 'But you'd like me to find out?' he challenged her.

'No. No, I wouldn't!' she protested. 'I prefer to be left alone!'

Manoel chuckled. 'You're very feminine,' he told her.

'I suppose so, seeing that I'm a woman!' she said tartly.

'All woman, yet you resent being reminded of the fact—'

'I do not!'

'Then I feel free to kiss you with impunity,' he teased her.

She glared at him. 'Women are not necessarily helpless!'

'You intrigue me,' he smiled.

'Well, your threats don't intrigue me!' she said crushingly.

He laughed again. 'I like to see you with your feathers ruffled,' he admired her. 'You're not at all the ice-cold maiden you'd like the world to believe. I was taken in for a few minutes myself,' he conceded handsomely.

She was afraid that she would say something that she would regret and so she finished her meal in what her brother would have called a 'speaking silence'. It was not good for Luis to see his elders openly quarrelling, she reminded herself, but the temptation was strong to tell the unspeakable Manoel Ferrado what she thought of him, once and for all, with no holds barred.

Manoel leaned forward across the table. 'Aren't you going to tell us what your first impression of me was?' he prompted her.

'No,' she said with commendable calm.

'I thought not.'

She opened her mouth, changed her mind, and shut it again.

'Yes?' he said.

'I thought you were not the kind of man that I should dream of working with,' she told him coolly.

'Naturally not!' he agreed with approval.

'Oh?' she enquired politely.

'I shouldn't care to *work* with you either!'

'But then you wouldn't work with any woman, would you? I haven't your prejudices about the opposite sex. I just like some members better than others.' She cast a swift glance in his direction and was annoyed to see that he was still smiling. His conceit, she decided, was beyond belief!

'But we have agreed that we have no need to like one another,' he reminded her slowly.

'Don't you like Camilla?' Luis demanded, his eyes as big as saucers.

His uncle smiled slowly. 'I take it that you do?' he said to the child.

Luis nodded his head vigorously. 'I like her very much,' he agreed. 'She doesn't fuss.'

Manoel's eyebrows rose. 'How differently we see people,' he observed. 'Have you finished eating? Then you may go up to your bed.'

Luis left the table reluctantly. 'Will you come and say goodnight to me?' he asked Camilla urgently.

'Indeed I will,' she reassured him. She thought privately that the boy should have been put straight to bed and given something to eat upstairs, but she knew that children on the Continent stayed up later than any English child, even on normal days, and this was hardly a normal day in any of their lives.

'I'll stay awake until you come,' he urged her.

'I'll come in ten—no, five minutes,' she promised him.

She watched him as he went round the table and said a formal goodnight to his uncle and smiled at him as he scampered out of the room and could be heard jumping up the stairs, two at a time.

'You are fond of the boy?' Manoel said gently.

She looked at him quickly. 'I hardly know him. I met both him and Leonor for the first time yesterday.'

'Indeed?' She thought he looked surprised. 'I should have thought your brother would have sought your approval before he committed himself to matrimony.'

'Why should he?' she retorted.

'It was no more than an impression I had received,' he said.

'Ah,' she said, 'you leaped to a conclusion!'

His startled, affronted face struck her as being very funny. 'Perhaps I was hasty,' he admitted judiciously, 'but I don't think so. I received this letter from my sister-in-law asking me to take care of Luis for the next few weeks and to act as his guardian during his childhood. This is a natural request. Luis is a Ferrado and he will have responsibilities accordingly when he is older.'

'Yet my brother is his stepfather,' Camilla reminded him firmly.

'That is not particularly important,' Manoel dismissed her comment. 'Now that my father is dead there is nothing to stop Luis coming into his inheritance. He must be prepared for this. It is not a simple matter.'

'But you are the elder son. Luis's father couldn't

have inherited all that much.'

'Enough.'

Camilla digested this in silence. It was incredible to her that Leonor should have written such a letter.

'Didn't she tell you that I was coming to Portugal to look after Luis while she and Dennis were honeymooning?' she asked humbly.

'No.'

'I can't understand it!' Camilla exclaimed.

'That is obvious,' he said quite kindly. 'You do not understand us at all. Nor will you believe me that Leonor would probably have been much happier had my brother done as I suggested in the first place. She would have found it more than pleasant to be Jaime's mistress. My family would have protected her and the child. She has never been able to come to terms with her position as Jaime's wife or widow. You see I am not as unkind as you wish to believe.'

'I think you old-fashioned,' Camilla said abruptly. 'What if your family is noble? It doesn't make a Ferrado a different kind of being, does it?'

'In some ways.'

Camilla bit her lip. 'I can almost believe it!' she said.

His eyes lit with amusement. 'Are we so strange?' he challenged her.

'I don't know. You're ruthless and you don't care who gets hurt if they stand in your way, do you? I have always been told that position meant more than just privilege and responsibility.'

'More?' he shot at her.

'Yes, more. It means kindness to your inferiors.'

He was silent for a minute. 'Are you going to give me an example?' he asked her.

'Leonor,' she said on a sigh.

'Leonor? Has she any cause for complaint?'

'You know she has!

He smiled. 'I thought you were going to cite yourself as an example.'

'Me?' she echoed.

'Yes, you. I think you need kindness more than most. I apologise for kissing you against your will, *senhorita*.' He smiled at her and she could feel her heart thudding against her ribs. He was a handsome devil when he chose to be, but he was not to be trusted. She must remember that! 'Was it against your will?' he added.

She was on the point of admitting that she had been partly responsible for the kiss, but she couldn't find the words to say anything at all.

'I must go and say goodnight to Luis!' she gasped. 'Goodnight, *senhor*.'

'Goodnight, *senhorita*,' he returned.

Camilla flew up the stairs, running away from the look in his eyes and her own astonishing reaction. Her colour was high and her eyes were very bright when she rushed into Luis's room.

'You look half asleep already,' she told him.

'I stayed awake, though,' he said proudly. 'Mama always kisses me goodnight. It's strange without her.'

'It won't be for long,' she said. 'It isn't the same, I know, but I'd like to kiss you goodnight for her while she's away.'

The boy thought about it. 'Your hair is the colour of honey,' he said at last. 'Does it smell like honey too?'

'Smell it and see,' she suggested.

He breathed in, wrinkling up his nose. 'Not honey exactly,' he opined, 'but it smells nice. This is a nice house, isn't it?' he added.

'Very nice,' she agreed promptly.

'But I'm glad you're staying here too,' he said sleepily. He reached up and kissed her warmly. 'Tio

Manoel isn't a bit like Papa was.'

'Are you afraid of him?' Camilla asked him before she could stop herself.

'Of Tio? No,' he said uncertainly. 'Are you?'

'Of course not!' Camilla laughed. She tucked the boy in and kissed him warmly on the cheek, a little surprised at herself for actually enjoying the little ceremony. 'Go to sleep,' she said.

In her own room, she scarcely noticed the maid asleep on the truckle bed at the foot of the fourposter. She went into the bathroom and undressed, creeping into bed without turning on the light for fear of waking the girl. She was a long time going to sleep, though. When she shut her eyes, she could feel Manoel's lips against her own, and she blushed to think of her own response to him. He would think that she enjoyed that sort of thing! She turned over restlessly and tried to banish the moment from her mind. Tomorrow, she thought, she would start on her new collection and this unsettled feeling would be as unimportant as it really was. But tomorrow was a long time coming.

## CHAPTER IV

'*Bom dia, senhorita.*'

Camilla opened her eyes slowly, a little surprised to find herself in the middle of the enormous fourposter bed.

'*Bom dia,*' she replied, her tongue tripping over the words. '*Não falo português.* I can't speak Portuguese,' she added quickly.

The maid giggled. 'I speak a little English,' she said proudly. 'I hope you slept well?'

Camilla nodded. She blinked up at the girl's face, dusky with sunshine. 'Did you?'

The maid giggled again. 'Yes, I sleep very well. But Senhorita Carlota will be very angry if I snore and disturb you.' The girl puzzled over something for a minute. 'Is it true that in England you sleep in a room by yourself?' she asked.

'Always,' Camilla said promptly.

'And you are not lonely—or frightened?'

Camilla shook her head. 'I've always had a room to myself,' she explained.

'But when you marry—?'

'I don't suppose I shall,' Camilla smiled. She saw that she had shocked the girl and was annoyed with herself. 'It's different when one is married,' she temporised.

The girl nodded enthusiastically. 'I shall be married myself soon,' she told Camilla happily. 'It must be the same with you! You are so beautiful. There must be many men who wish to marry with you.'

'I don't know,' Camilla murmured, more to herself than to the maid. 'I've always been too busy to consider getting married. Camilla Enterprises is a jealous taskmaster one way and another.'

The girl dismissed that as nonsense, even while she didn't understand much of what Camilla had been saying.

'*O Duque* has brought you to his house,' she said, her voice alive with interest. 'Perhaps he has a liking for you?'

Camilla was startled into silence. 'I thought the house belonged to the Senhor Ferrado?'

The girl nodded. 'O Senhor Duque de Ferrado. It is his house.'

'Duke?' Camilla repeated hoarsely.

'*Sim*,' the girl said simply. 'He has never brought another lady to his house, though there have been many rumours, as is natural with such a man. It is said by

52

some that he is affianced to the Condessa Victoria Arrabida, but now that you are here—' She shrugged expressively.

' I am only here to look after Luis,' Camilla told her quickly.

' So it is said,' the maid agreed. ' I bring your breakfast here, *minha menina?*'

Camilla hesitated. ' No,' she said. ' I think I'll have breakfast downstairs with Luis.'

' *Sim, minha menina.*'

Camilla dressed herself rapidly, determinedly ignoring the sinking feeling in the pit of her stomach. He was, she reminded herself, still the same man whether he was a duke or a dustman. It was a strangely unconvincing argument.

In consequence, she was highly put out to discover that Manoel had come downstairs before her.

' *Vossa Excelência!*' she greeted him dourly.

He had the audacity to grin at her. ' Who told you?' he asked her.

' Not you!' she answered pointedly.

' Portugal is a republic these days,' he said indifferently.

She pretended not to have heard him, sweeping into the dining room before him, her head held high.

' If I had known that you were going to be so impressed, I might have told you sooner,' he informed her back.

' I am not in the least impressed!'

' Then why are you so angry?'

' I think you might have told me,' she said resentfully. ' And not just left me to find out from the maid!'

' How was I to know you would gossip with my servants?' he enquired mildly.

She stamped her foot at him. ' I do *not* gossip!'

' All women gossip,' he said with certainty. ' It is

53

the major pastime of all my female relatives, I assure you.'

'Really?' she said bluntly. 'Well, I'm too busy to gossip!' She glared at him, but he made no attempt to say anything further. 'I still think you might have told me yourself!' she went on in aggrieved tones.

'Why? Would you have preferred to have been kissed by a duke?'

She faced him bravely. 'Unworthy,' she commented.

His eyes met hers. 'Yes, I think it was,' he admitted. 'Will you accept my apology?'

'For the kiss?'

'No, never for that!'

Camilla blushed. It was ridiculous, she knew, but she couldn't have borne to have him apologise for that. 'I—I accept your apology,' she stammered, and blushed again.

'Thank you,' he said soberly. 'Then I shall ring for your breakfast? I am told that Luis is having his in bed, so you will only have myself for company.'

But in the end she had breakfast alone, for Manoel was called away to take a telephone call and he never returned to finish his breakfast at all. This was hardly something to cry about, Camilla assured herself, but it did give her a lowering feeling that set the tone for the whole of the rest of the day. At lunchtime, he had still not returned and at dinner he had an engagement to fulfil on the other side of Lisbon and was sure that she and Luis would not miss him.

Luis did not. He found the change from the rough and ready home that he had always shared with his mother to the formal atmosphere of Manoel's town mansion hard to manage. He had visited the house before, he assured Camilla, though only since his grandfather had died, but he had never lived there for twenty-four hours a day and it wasn't the sort of house that one could play games in, or shout to one's friends out of the windows.

'Will we have to stay here all the time?' he asked Camilla that evening.

'Until your mother and Dennis come home,' she told him.

'That will be *ages*. There's been nothing to do all day!'

Camilla felt guilty. She had done very little to entertain Luis, she thought. She hadn't the remotest idea what kind of thing a small boy of his age would want to do. Nor had she done anything much herself. Manoel disturbed her concentration and made her unlike herself. She had always known exactly what she wanted out of life and she preferred it that way. But today, she had been moody and wanted she knew not what, though she was gloomily aware that it was something to do with Manoel and the easy way he stirred up emotions she had never known she had.

'We have lots to do,' she said aloud. 'Tomorrow we'll go out and take a look at Lisbon. How's that?'

The boy nodded seriously. 'I shall show you everything,' he agreed. 'But what shall we do after that?'

Camilla considered for a moment. 'I have work to do,' she told him. 'I have a collection to get together—'

'Will I be able to help you?'

'I suppose so. Do you like drawing and painting?'

Luis smiled angelically. 'Real paints?'

'Of course with real paints. It isn't worth anyone's while to try and work without the proper tools.'

'I think I'll paint you,' Luis said, much pleased.

'Well—if you want to,' Camilla agreed uncertainly. 'Wouldn't you rather draw a picture of your uncle?'

Luis shook his head. 'He hasn't got honey-coloured hair.'

'He's very handsome, though,' Camilla said

55

dreamily.

'I want to paint you,' Luis repeated, his lower lip
jutting forward in stubborn decision. '*You* can paint
Tio Manoel!'

Camilla could feel herself colouring at the thought.
'I couldn't!' she exclaimed without thought. 'Besides,'
she added on a firmer note, 'it would hardly help my
collection along, would it?'

'I don't know,' Luis answered her. 'I don't know
what your collection is.'

Camilla spent a long time telling him about it. She did
a series of little drawings to show him how she went
about designing her range of clothes, household
materials, handbags, and everything else that went to
make up Camilla Enterprises.

'You start with one simple line,' she ended, 'and
then you find that everything else is wrong and that they
all have to be fitted in as well. Last year's shoes never
go with this year's skirts. It's a fact of life.'

Luis picked up her pencil and began to do one or two
drawings of his own. She watched his efforts with
interest as he drew a rough sketch of his mother, her
black fisherwoman's shawl over her head, just as she
wore it when she was singing in one of the *fado* houses
of Lisbon.

'She always wears the same,' the boy said with
satisfaction.

'Hmph,' Camilla commented. 'I shouldn't make
much money out of her, then?'

'No. Dennis is going to buy her lots of new clothes,
though,' he confided. 'I expect he'll buy some of them
from you.'

Camilla refrained from laughing. Where else would
Dennis buy his wife's clothes? 'I expect so,' she said
gently.

'But your clothes won't suit Mama,' Luis said flatly.

'Then we'll have to design something specially for her,' Camilla suggested.

Luis looked pleased. 'Yes, yes, I will help you! I will help you, won't I?'

'Indeed you will,' Camilla assured him.

She slept no better the second night in Manoel's house than she had the first. She and Luis had more in common than she had thought, for she too was over-awed by her surroundings, especially by *the fourposter bed*. It loomed over her in the darkness and, coupled with the slight sound of the maid sleeping at her feet, it was quite enough to keep anyone awake.

In the morning Camilla decided she looked so haggard that she would accept the quietly offered invitation to bring her breakfast in bed.

'The dining room is rather big when one is on one's own,' she excused herself fretfully to the maid.

'*O Duque* is there already,' she answered.

Camilla pulled the bedclothes up closer about her. 'All the same—' she said.

She was barely dressed when Luis came in to fetch her. The small boy sauntered round her room while she put the finishing touches to her make-up.

'Where are we going first?' he asked her repeatedly.

'I'm expecting you to take me,' she answered. 'Lisbon is your city.'

'I'll take you to the Jerónimos Monastery, and the Tower of Belem, and the monument to the Discoverers, *everything*!' he said expansively.

'Right you are,' she said easily. 'I'm ready when you are!'

They descended the stairs together to find Manoel waiting for them in the hall below.

'We have guests coming for morning coffee,' he announced. 'I trust you will both be here to receive them.'

'Well,' Camilla began slowly, 'Luis was going to show me something of Lisbon.'

'There's time enough for that,' Manoel replied irritably.

Camilla merely looked at him in silence. Luis drew a pattern on the deep carpet with the toe of his shoe. 'I don't want to have coffee,' he said.

'One has to learn to be polite!'

'Camilla doesn't want coffee either,' the boy continued.

His uncle turned on him. 'That's enough! And if you must call the *senhorita* by her Christian name, you had better call her Tia Camilla.'

Luis looked uncertainly at Camilla. 'I'm not his aunt,' she said stoically.

'You are by marriage.'

She couldn't help feeling that he looked rather splendid even when he was irritable. The strong, mobile mouth betrayed his feelings more than any other feature, more even than his black, enigmatic eyes. She realised that she was staring at him and that he was looking questioningly at her, and she blushed.

'Who—who is coming to coffee?' she asked hastily.

'Dona Victoria Arrabida and her mother.'

Camilla could not hide her interest. 'Oh,' she said.

Manoel frowned at her. 'She comes fairly often,' he said repressively. 'I am anxious that she should not get the wrong impression of your visit here.'

'Naturally,' Camilla said.

He shot another look at her. 'Our families have been friends for many generations.'

Camilla's eyes danced with sudden amusement. 'Really?' she said casually.

He took a quick breath. 'Why not?' he asked sharply.

Camilla felt ashamed. 'No reason. I'm sure she's

very nice. What time is she coming?'

'Any time now,' he answered warmly. 'I think you'll like her,' he added quietly. He pushed open the door to the family sitting room and stood aside for Camilla to precede him into the room. She took a step forward and then stopped.

'Duke,' she began, 'I didn't mean to get at you—'

'I think you had better call me Manoel,' he interrupted her. 'Duke sounds a little too like your favourite labrador!'

She chuckled. 'I should have thought you'd be used to it!' she retorted.

'I suppose I should be,' he admitted, 'but I hardly know anyone who calls me by my title.'

'I don't suppose they dare!' she teased him.

'No,' he agreed quite seriously; 'they are either my friends or my inferiors.'

Camilla winced. 'I wouldn't know about that,' she said witheringly. 'I haven't got any!'

She thought she saw his lips twitch, but his face was quite expressionless as he said, 'That could be true.'

Camilla cast him a speaking look and squeezed past him into the sitting room. He made no effort to get out of her way and she couldn't help touching him. The effect on her was immediate and infinitely shocking to her. She felt winded and a fountain of excitement rose within her. He, on the other hand, looked completely unmoved. She doubted that he had even noticed.

Camilla sat down on the sofa, irritated with herself for being vulnerable where any man was concerned. It had never happened to her before and she was quite sure that it was merely a case for mind over matter and she would be what she had always been, calm, cool and collected, and with the satisfaction of being successful in her own field as well.

Luis came and sat beside her, his disappointment that

they were not going out plain to see.

'I know the Dona Victoria,' he muttered.

'Where did you meet her?' Camilla asked him.

'She was here one day when I came. She doesn't like Mama.'

Camilla had the satisfaction of seeing Manoel look uncomfortable at this remark.

'Perhaps she has never met your mama,' Camilla said soothingly.

'She has!' Luis shouted indignantly. 'She has seen her sing! She came to the *fado* house one night. I saw her there, but she didn't see me!'

Manoel frowned. 'I think you are mistaken,' he told his nephew abruptly.

'I'm not! I'm not! I saw her there!'

'Alone?' Manoel asked scathingly.

The boy nodded, his eyes full of unshed tears. He looked very like his uncle at that moment. 'Mama spoke to her,' he insisted.

'I don't believe you,' Manoel said flatly. 'And I won't have you repeating lies about my friends.'

Camilla took Luis's hand into her own, giving him a reassuring squeeze.

'I don't see why Dona Victoria shouldn't go to hear Leonor sing if she wants to,' she murmured. 'She has the most fantastic voice.'

'That is not the point,' Manoel snapped.

'No?'

'She would never have gone alone to such a place!'

Camilla laughed in the back of her throat. 'Why ever not? Is this another of your Portuguese customs?'

'We protect our women,' Manoel said brittlely.

'From yourselves?' she asked pointedly.

He glared at her. 'We are not cold like your Englishmen—'

'So you arrange matters to suit yourselves,' she

finished for him. 'Potential wives are protected from all comers, while the rest are fair game.'

He shrugged. 'It's the way things are,' he said dismissively.

'How nice!' she commented.

'It gives security to our women—' he began grandly.

'To the Victorias,' she consented. 'Hardly to the Leonors.' Her eyes swept up to meet his. 'Which category do I come in?'

Manoel was taken aback by such a direct approach. 'I refuse to discuss the matter with you any further,' he said angrily.

'I see. You forget that I am an Englishwoman and accustomed to look after myself! *I'm* not prepared to take my role in life at the hands of any man!'

His anger died away and for a moment he looked amused. 'Hadn't you better wait until you're asked?'

Camilla felt the burning colour rise like a tide in her cheeks. It was no comfort that he should wilfully misunderstand her. She caught the tail end of the triumphant light in his dark eyes and resolved that she wouldn't give him the satisfaction of ever getting the better verbally of her again.

As it was, she was grateful for a sudden flurry of activity in the hall, announcing the arrival of the Dona Victoria and her mother. She looked up expectantly as the door opened and Manoel's manservant bowed as the two women walked into the room. Camilla's first reaction was that they were not as smart as she had expected. Indeed, the Dona Victoria was a small, dumpy woman, though she was not yet as fat as her mother who followed her into the room, looking both nervous and dismayed.

Dona Victoria's eyes went from Manoel's face to Camilla's and her mouth compressed with disapproval at the sight of them together.

'Manoel! *Bom dia. Como está?*' She allowed Manoel to kiss her hand, nodding complacently towards her mother.

'Senhorita Armstrong does not speak Portuguese,' Manoel warned her in English.

Dona Victoria frowned. 'How awkward,' she commented briefly. 'My mother's English is extremely indifferent.'

Camilla ignored her, greeting the elder woman first. '*Muito prazer*,' she murmured as Manoel introduced them and was rewarded by a beaming smile. Dona Victoria looked far from pleased.

'Are you here long?' she asked in clear, ringing tones.

'No, *minha senhora*,' Camilla answered politely.

'I suppose not,' Dona Victoria approved. 'Jaime's marriage was bad enough, but the consequences are proving more and more awkward to poor Manoel.'

'Really?' Camilla said smoothly. She could not resist shooting a glance at Manoel to see how he liked being addressed as 'poor Manoel', but he was smiling at Dona Victoria's mother as she recounted a long and rambling story and had apparently not heard her daughter's words at all.

'Of course none of *us* know Leonor—'

'I love her dearly,' Camilla interrupted.

'You've met her?' The Condessa gave her a look that was deliciously naughty. 'Is she—is she all they say?'

'What do they say?' Camilla asked innocently.

Dona Victoria looked bashful. 'I suppose she is very voluptuous?'

Camilla laughed softly. 'Is that what you thought of her? I suppose she does give that impression. There's more to her than meets the eye.'

'As your brother discovered?'

'And Jaime before him,' Camilla returned imperturbably.

Dona Victoria tightened her mouth. 'That was quite unsuitable.' She glanced at Luis, who had gone to stand beside his uncle. 'Poor Manoel!' she breathed.

Camilla felt her temper getting the better of her. 'I make it a practice never to feel sorry for dukes,' she said.

Dona Victoria's mouth became a small knot in her face. 'Have you met many?' she asked sweetly.

Camilla smiled with a touch of mischief. 'No, thank goodness, I've been spared knowing too many of them!'

'Snob!' Manoel put in from across the room.

'Not at all. I prefer people who are admired for their own merits, not for something their ancestors were or did.'

The Dona Victoria muttered something in Portuguese and received a warning look from her mother. 'It is a novel idea to such a person as myself,' she said in English. 'I find you so—so quaint!'

Manoel came and stood over them both. 'England is a topsy-turvy world to our way of thinking,' he agreed. 'Senhorita Armstrong appears to have no one to look after her. Even her brother works for her, isn't this so?'

'In a way,' Camilla agreed uncomfortably.

'But,' Dona Victoria enquired with the air of someone determined to get to the root of the matter, 'but, my dear, who will find a husband for you? I have been told your father is no longer alive, but surely your mother and your brother feel this responsibility very much?'

Camilla winced. 'My mother—no!' she exclaimed before she could stop herself.

'Your brother must do so,' Dona Victoria pressed her.

'I don't think so,' Camilla said repressively. 'Why should he? If I wanted to marry, I can find my own husband.'

63

Both Portuguese women looked thoroughly scandalised. 'It won't be a *husband* you'll find!' Dona Victoria warned her grimly.

'I think that is my business,' Camilla said quietly.

The Condessa's mother shook her head sadly, clicking her tongue against her teeth. 'The poor child!' she exclaimed.

Camilla stiffened. 'There is absolutely no need to feel *sorry* for me—' she began.

'Should we rather envy your success?' Manoel asked smoothly.

Camilla fought with her rising temper. She swallowed, employing a gambit she had learned when dealing with a peculiarly awkward customer.

'Not if you don't want to.' She smiled coolly. 'I can see that you don't buy your clothes in London, Paris, or New York—you could hardly have avoided buying something of ours if you did—but perhaps we shall expand to Lisbon one day.'

'You sell men's clothes?' Manoel said, startled.

'Of course,' she said briefly.

'But how can *you* design clothes for men?' Dona Victoria demanded, shocked by the very idea.

'Why not?' Camilla sounded amused.

Dona Victoria looked embarrassed. 'Well, if you don't know—' She allowed her voice to trail away in disgust. 'But a *woman* to design a *man's* clothing!'

'I don't see that it's any different from a man designing a woman's clothes,' Camilla objected. 'Do you, duke?'

She had the pleasure of seeing Manoel wince at her use of his title. He was right, she thought, it did sound rather as though she were addressing her favourite dog.

'In principle, no,' he admitted pleasantly enough.

Luis, tired of being ignored, chose this moment to come to Camilla's defence. 'Tia Camilla has only to write her name on something for it to be very expensive in London,' he informed them all solemnly. 'I have heard Mama say so.'

'And she would know, I suppose?' Dona Victoria said unkindly.

Luis looked at her with an unblinking stare. 'I think she does,' he said.

Dona Victoria sniffed. 'So loyal!' she muttered.

Camilla allowed her gaze to travel slowly over the other woman. She wondered if she had ever disliked anyone more on first sight. 'But then you don't know Leonor, do you?' she said sweetly.

To her surprise she caught a wicked glimpse of laughter in the Condessa's mother's eyes. 'Will you have some more coffee, *minha senhora*?' she asked the older woman with a touch of desperation, aware that she had been on the point of rudeness.

'Thank you,' the Portuguese woman lisped carefully. 'It would be nice if we were all to be less formal, don't you think? Please, you must call me Joana, for I am going to call you by this pretty name of yours, Camilla. I have not heard it before, but then you are quite right, it is many years since I did any shopping in London.'

Camilla coloured faintly. 'You look lovely,' she said awkwardly.

'I have no figure to look lovely! Since my husband died I have no one to please but myself and I am very fond of food.' She leaned forward towards Camilla. 'So is my daughter,' she whispered.

'Mama!' Dona Victoria rebuked her.

Dona Joana sighed. 'It is the truth,' she said positively. 'You will find that Portuguese women are not elegant like the Spanish, but we are often told that we are nicer! Manoel will tell you!' The twinkle reached her eyes again. 'His experience is *vast*, I can tell you!'

'*Mama!*' Dona Victoria breathed faintly.

Camilla laughed. 'Did you go and hear Leonor sing too, *senhora*?' she asked her slyly.

'That is a big secret!' Dona Joana laughed. 'I was of the opinion that the family should have accepted her, especially after—' She nodded in Luis's direction.

'But Manoel's father was a stiff man!'

'It was impossible!' Dona Victoria said in stifled tones. 'There were other people to be considered. Manoel might have married—'

Dona Joana shrugged. 'I think I should like her very well,' she announced placidly. 'If Camilla likes her, so will I!'

Dona Victoria flushed. 'I prefer to change the subject,' she said with dignity. 'Manoel, do you escort us to the dance on Thursday?'

Manoel smiled lazily. 'I think not. I am thinking of taking Luis to the *quinta* near Navaré. It is time he took an interest in his estate.'

'And this is more important?' Dona Victoria snapped.

Camilla felt suddenly sorry for Manoel if he was indeed going to marry the Condessa. She thought that he would find very little fun in his household if she was to be mistress of it.

'To me it is,' Manoel said gently.

'But *I* am going to the dance,' Dona Victoria reminded him. 'It will look so odd if I go without you!'

'Then you had better stay away,' Dona Joana put in maliciously.

'I shall have to go! I am not in mourning! Manoel, what excuse shall I give for you not being there?'

Manoel smiled lazily across at her. 'I shall make my own excuses.'

The Condessa gave Luis and Camilla an all-embracing look of pure hatred. 'Oh, very well!' she said.

66

Luis ate his lunch with every sign of enjoyment. As a concession to him, the housekeeper had ordered a fisherman's stew, full of a variety of local fish, freshly caught that morning, and cooked with peppers and other vegetables. It reminded Luis of home and he had three helpings to show them that it was one of his favourite dishes.

' It isn't as good as Mama's,' he told Camilla. ' But it's very good, isn't it?'

Camilla agreed that it was. She was spending her time studiously avoiding Manoel's eyes. This afternoon, she determined, she and Luis would go sight seeing no matter what. A breath of fresh air was badly needed by them all.

' Where will you go?' Manoel asked her with that uncanny knack he had of picking up her thoughts.

' I don't know,' she admitted. ' Luis is going to show me his Lisbon.'

Luis immediately looked important. ' We're going to look at the Monastery and other things,' he announced.

' Why don't you take her to the Castle?' his uncle suggested.

But Luis shook his head. ' Not today. Tio, may we go across the river tonight? Can we have dinner over there? Will you come with us?'

Manoel smiled at him. ' If you like,' he agreed lazily.

Luis cast Camilla a look of triumph. ' That will be better than anything!' he told her. ' Mama and I do that often, whenever we are feeling lonely.'

' And are you feeling lonely now?' Camilla asked him gently.

' A little bit,' he admitted. ' I don't like Dona

Victoria—'

'That's enough, Luis,' Manoel headed him off.

'It isn't enough!' the boy protested. '*She* doesn't like Mama!'

'She doesn't know her, so she can't either like or dislike your mother,' Manoel said gruffly.

Luis glared across the table mutinously. 'She knows her!'

'That's enough!' Manoel repeated.

Luis sat back in his chair and grinned suddenly. 'Camilla doesn't like her!'

Camilla blushed. 'How do you know?' she demanded hotly.

To her surprise both the Ferrados burst out laughing. 'Be quiet, Luis!' Manoel chided his nephew softly.

'Well?' Camilla said angrily.

'I thought the honours were about even myself,' Manoel drawled.

Luis had another fit of giggles. 'She's *horrid*!' he said with decision.

'Luis!'

Camilla shrugged her shoulders. 'At least he's honest,' she said with a laugh. 'I like her mother, though.'

'That was obvious,' Manoel told her. 'It's fortunate for Victoria that her position is quite secure without needing a testimonial from either of you.'

Camilla's amusement died away. 'Is she a countess in her own right?' she enquired.

'She inherited the title from her father,' Manoel confirmed. 'She is an only child.'

And she wasn't content with being a mere countess, Camilla thought to herself. Dona Victoria would enjoy being the Duchess of Ferrado. But what would Manoel get out of it? The Condessa was already set in her ways and she would not appreciate having to conform her ideas to those of her husband. Yet Camilla couldn't imagine Manoel easily relinquishing his position as head of the household, even to the Condessa Victoria!

Camilla enjoyed her afternoon sightseeing with Luis. Although it was November the sun was shining brightly and it was warm enough for her to leave her coat behind and to wear no more than a simple dress. She felt like a child on a spree herself as they left the formal surroundings of the Ferrado town house behind them. What did interest her, however, were the famous tiles that completely covered the outside of the house. These were the famous Portuguese *azulejos*, a reminder of the strong Moorish influence that is to be found all over the country. Camilla found them beautiful and very practical. After all, once your house was tiled there was no need to repaint the exterior ever again.

'It is good against the humidity from the river,' Luis assured her knowledgeably. 'The oldest ones are all blue, the coloured ones came in later. Some black ones are very old, though.'

Camilla promised herself that she would find a book on the subject and read it up for herself. The designs on the tiles appealed to her and she thought that Dennis had been right when he had said that she might find them an inspiration for her new fabric designs. On cotton, she thought, the patterns would look clean and crisp, and there was no end to the variety of designs and colours.

'The Jerónimos Monastery is beautiful!' Luis sighed. 'It is older than this house, of course. You see, the monastery was there before the earthquake.'

'Oh?' Camilla encouraged him.

The boy nodded soberly. 'It was All Saints' Day and the royal family were all at High Mass in the monastery. Otherwise they all would have been killed. The palace fell down with everything else. Only the Alfama district, where we live, was safe. All the rest of Lisbon had to be rebuilt.'

Camilla couldn't help being glad that the monastery, at least, had survived. It was an impressively large building with a very ornate entrance. Inside, Luis dragged her straight off to the cloisters.

'They are beautiful, Camilla! They were built at the time of the Discoveries! You must see them!'

She saw at once what it was that appealed to him so much. The double arches glinted gold in the sunlight and were grey in the shadows. They were decorated with the symbols of the period, recalling the ships that the Discoverers had set out in to find the new world. There were carved ropes and anchors, replicas of the ships themselves, the cross of the Order of Christ, and the belted globe towering high in the sky.

'This style is called Manoeline,' Luis explained. 'Manoel I was king at that time.'

They walked right round the cloisters and into a small chapel where an echo had been deliberately built into the acoustics to produce the famous sound for which the monastery had once been renowned. Luis was soon bored with demonstrating how the music was repeated, rather like a round song, and suggested they took a look at the tomb of Vasco da Gama before they left.

'He shouldn't be here,' Luis said stoutly. 'His family had him buried in their family vault. He was only brought here in modern times. His family refused to have him moved, but they moved him in the end just the same.'

'I suppose they thought he belonged to the Portuguese people as well as to his own family,' Camilla suggested.

'Y-yes,' Luis agreed doubtfully. 'But his family should come first. Mama says so!'

'Does she?' Camilla said, interested.

'One's family is one's background,' Luis explained

simply. 'The nation is rather big for that, don't you think? Mama says I must always remember I am a Ferrado and that their traditions are mine.'

'And what do you think?' Camilla asked him.

Luis turned away from her sadly. 'Mama isn't a Ferrado,' he said bleakly. 'They wouldn't accept her. She says they couldn't because she is a *varina* before she married. She says she was a very good *varina*—she sold more fish than anyone else, so I am not to be ashamed of her.'

Camilla looked at him kindly. 'I think you are lucky in your mother,' she said. 'She sold more fish than anyone else and she was a famous singer besides! What did your father do?'

'He was a Ferrado!' Luis said with conscious pride. 'He didn't have to do anything!'

'I prefer your mother!' Camilla exclaimed darkly.

Luis laughed. 'That's because you are English, like Dennis. What is your mother like?'

Camilla bit her lip. 'She's very gay,' she answered. 'She likes to have lots of different people around her all the time.'

'Is she like you?' Luis asked her shyly.

'No!' Camilla snapped.

Luis began to walk out of the monastery, squinting into the sunlight. 'Tio Manoel said she was like you,' he informed her casually. 'That she is fair and beautiful, and laughed a lot.'

Camilla felt both hurt and angry. 'I don't think your uncle knows her very well,' she said dryly.

Luis stared at her, his eyes wide. 'Don't you like her?' he demanded in shocked tones.

Camilla was on the point of saying that of course she liked her mother, but when it came to it, she couldn't say it. 'I don't know her very well either,' she said finally. 'She was always at some party or other when

Dennis and I lived with her. She hadn't much time for us.'

'Oh,' said Luis. 'Wasn't your father with you?'

'No, he went away a long time ago,' Camilla told him. 'Is he dead?'

Camilla shook her head. 'I don't think so. I don't really know,' she admitted. 'I can hardly remember him at all. Dennis is supposed to be quite like him.'

'I thought he might be dead like my father,' Luis said on a sigh. 'If he were dead, your mother could marry again like mine.'

Camilla smiled rather sourly. 'I can't see my mother marrying again,' she remarked.

'Why not?'

'You have to love someone very much to marry them,' she said with a touch of embarrassment.

'Like Mama loves Dennis?'

Camilla nodded. 'My mother enjoys being fancy free and having lots of men interested in her—'

Luis frowned. 'I thought all women wanted a husband', he interrupted her. 'Don't you?'

'I haven't had time to think about it,' Camilla said with a laugh. 'I have to work, you see.'

Luis accepted this thoughtfully. 'I think you like Tio Manoel,' he said at last in clear, ringing tones.

'But not as a husband!' she protested.

Luis favoured her with a gamin grin. '*He* wouldn't make you work hard,' he consoled her.

'But I like working hard!'

'Tio Manoel would give you everything you want. He has to marry, you see,' he went on practically, 'and, as you're English, it wouldn't matter that you are not a Condessa.'

'Certainly not!' Camilla retorted huffily. 'I don't suppose his family would accept me either!' she added unnecessarily.

Luis chuckled. 'Tio Manoel would have to accept his own wife!' he teased her, finding the idea a good joke. 'He's the head of the family!'

But Camilla only grunted. The thought of Manoel as a husband was one which took her breath away. She had planned her life with care and she intended to follow that plan to the end. Manoel might be able to make her heart flutter in the most alarming way, but no man was worth giving up her independence and her right to exist in her own right. Besides, Manoel would look to his own kind for a wife. He would look where he was looking now, straight into the greedy eyes of the Condessa Victoria Arrabida!

The queue for the ferry to go across the River Tagus was a long one. Luis jumped up and down excitedly as they approached the edge of the jetty.

'Will we go on this boat, Tio Manoel?'

'The next one,' Manoel answered certainly. 'And a good thing too! There may be a little more room on the next one.'

'But I like all the people,' the boy protested.

Manoel put his hand on Camilla's elbow to guide her down the heavy gangway. 'And do you like the people too?' he asked her.

She side-stepped round a large woman, glad of the excuse to free herself from Manoel's touch. 'This is fun!' she laughed at them both.

They shoved their way onto the boat in company with a hundred other people. Luis made a rush for a small open space in the front, scorning the wooden seat that his uncle had found for the three of them. Camilla sat down gratefully, looking back at the Praça do Comércio. To one side she could see the lights of the new bridge across the Tagus that had only recently been completed. It was supposed to be a copy of the famous Golden Gate of San Francisco and, eventually, the idea was that the trains would also cross on the lower part of the bridge, but as yet there was no money in the kitty for such a grandiose scheme.

The ferry lurched away from the jetty, turning slowly away from the city. There were fewer lights on the other side of the river. The statue of Christ Regnant, put up by the Portuguese hierarchy in thanksgiving for Portuguese neutrality in the last war, floated in the darkness, the arms outstretched in blessing over the beloved capital resting on its seven hills.

More people poured on to the ferry and Camilla was obliged to move closer to Manoel. She was very conscious of the feel of his leg against hers and sat up very straight, berating herself inwardly for being a fool.

Manoel laughed softly in her ear and she had the horrid feeling that he had picked up her thoughts again. He put his arm around her shoulders and pulled her close against him.

' If they allow many more people on this bench we shall not be able to breathe!' he observed.

Camilla didn't answer. She concentrated hard on her breathing in case he should think that his action had had any effect on her. He didn't look much like a duke, sitting there, waiting for the ferry to nose its way into the jetty on the other side. He looked— But she refused to think about him at all!

' What do you do to make your hair that colour?' Manoel asked suddenly.

' Nothing!' Camilla retorted indignantly.

His disbelief was obvious. ' It was the colour of her hair that made me notice your mother,' he told her. ' Are you going to tell me that hers is natural also?'

' Why not?' she asked rigidly.

He shrugged and the movement recalled to her senses how very close he was to her. ' When a woman is of a certain age such very fair hair is apt to fade,' he smiled.

She jumped away from him and was obliged to apologise to her neighbour on the other side. ' I don't know about my mother,' she admitted. ' I don't know *anything* about my mother, but I don't have to do anything to my own hair. You'd be able to see at the roots if I did!'

He put up a hand and pulled gently at a loose tendril of her hair, pretending to examine it closely.

' Do you ever wear it loose?' he murmured.

' Only in bed,' she answered, and then she blushed. She looked down at her hands in her lap and tried to control the rising flood of colour that she had no hope of hiding from his interested eyes.

' Indeed?' he said. ' Don't you ever wear it loose in the evenings?'

' No,' she said tautly. ' I hate it flopping about my shoulders, if you must know!'

' Because it doesn't go with the cool image you like to present to the world?' he teased her.

' It's untidy—'

' And feminine,' he taunted her. ' It would go better with the warmth of your lips. Why do you pretend to have no feelings?'

' Because I prefer life that way!' she insisted.

His hand fell from her hair to trace the line of her jaw. ' Whatever makes you think that?' he drawled.

Her heart jumped within her. ' I don't want to get involved!'

' Why not? It would be a pleasure to make love to you!' She heard his light laugh against her ear and then felt his lips on her cheek.

' Because that sort of thing doesn't last,' she said primly. She thought he would surely hear the pounding of her heart and pulled away from him. If this went on she would turn into his embrace, she wouldn't be able to stop herself, and that would be the end of her carefully erected principles.

'Luis is right,' he said, 'your hair does smell like honey.'

'Manoel, don't!' she pleaded.

He chuckled. 'Can you honestly say you don't like it?'

She pulled herself together with an effort. 'I don't like the results,' she managed. 'I don't want my life to be—untidy and full of regrets and half-finished episodes. And that's all I'd ever be to you!'

'Mmm,' he murmured. 'Perhaps.'

'Perhaps?' She found it easy to be angry and she felt a great deal safer. 'There's no perhaps about it! You forget that you've told me all about these Portuguese customs of yours and they're not for me!'

'You tempt me to find out,' he said mockingly.

She bit her lip. 'But you won't!' she said sharply.

'I seldom resist temptation, but I'm open to persuasion,' he smiled.

The ferry shuddered to a stop, jarring against the jetty, and the passengers rushed to the gangway to get off. Camilla's relief was so obvious that Manoel's dark eyes openly mocked her as she hurried away from him, saying that she wanted to find Luis before he got lost in the crowds. Manoel followed more slowly, smiling faintly, in a knowing way that disturbed her more than his touch. He looked so *sure* of himself, and she had never felt more uncertain.

In the end it was Luis who found her, clasping her hand and helping her ashore with the natural good manners that seem bred in the bone of every Portuguese male.

'Don't you think Lisbon is a beautiful city?' he prompted her from the edge of the jetty. 'Look at the lights! You can see the road that goes over the bridge as it rises above the houses. Mama says this is the best view one can have of the whole city.'

It was indeed beautiful. The Tagus is two and a half kilometres wide in places at Lisbon and there is a good deal of traffic going up and down the river, little bobbing lights of green and red and white. And beyond is the long line of lights of Lisbon, with St George's Castle looking red and remote and the other notable buildings picked out by floodlights from the surrounding darkness.

Manoel caught up with them and, putting an arm round each of them, hurried them up the ramp and round the corner, away from the jetty, to where the lights of a workmen's bar streamed out across the road, almost hiding the entrance to the promenade along the side of the river.

'Are you hungry, Tio? I'm *very* hungry!'

'You should have had more fishermen's stew for lunch,' Manoel said solemnly.

'You could have had *four* helpings,' Camilla added.

'I didn't have room then,' Luis answered, equally serious. 'Where are we going to eat?'

There were several restaurants along the edge of the river. In the summer, Manoel told her, most Lisboans would come across the river from time to time and sit out the long evenings, admiring the city that they loved so well.

'It is one of the things that all Lisboans do, whether they are rich or poor. It is a little like *fado* in that way. It is something which everyone does.'

'Even dukes?' Camilla said dryly.

'Why not?' he countered. 'A duke is only a man.'

She blushed. 'Oh, surely not!' she exclaimed demurely.

'One day I shall show you,' he threatened complacently. 'What will you do then?'

77

'Go back to England!' she said promptly.

His eyebrows rose in disbelief. 'We shall see,' he remarked.

She turned her back on him huffily. 'Don't be silly,' she said in tones that she usually reserved for the younger members of her design team at home and only then when they were too busy playing the fool to get some order completed on time.

Manoel refused to take her at all seriously. He gave her a playful slap and laughed straight in her face.

'Poor Camilla!' he said.

'I'm not!' she denied desperately. 'I'm perfectly happy as I am!'

His whole expression challenged her. 'I don't believe you,' he said.

'How conceited can you get?' she stormed back at him. 'I like living alone, without any commitments and without any casual relationships. Is that so peculiar? Why should every woman spend her whole time waiting for some man to honour her with his attention? I prefer to depend on nobody's interest but my own!'

'Why?'

She was afraid that she was going to cry. 'I've seen too much—' she began, and broke off, swallowing down her tears.

'My dear, must you take everything so seriously?' he asked her very gently.

Camilla shook her head, striving for her usual self-control. 'I don't,' she retorted proudly. 'I don't take you seriously at all!'

A light wind had blown up, ruffling the water in front of them.

'Come on,' Manoel said in quite different tones. 'Let's go and get something to eat.'

He ushered them into the nearest restaurant and Camilla noticed how quickly the waiter came out to greet them and to find them a table. Manoel himself seemed to take the attentions of those around him as a matter of course. She played with the idea that the proprietor of the restaurant knew who he was, but she dismissed the thought as being ridiculous. It was something else about him that called attention to him and made people pleased to serve him.

'What will you have to drink?' he asked her.

'S-some wine,' she stammered.

He nodded gravely and embarked on a long discussion with the waiter as to which wine would suit her best. At last, satisfied, he turned back to her and smiled.

'The wine of the house seems fairly good,' he told her with satisfaction. 'I think you will enjoy it and it is suitable for Luis as well.'

It was a pleasant meal. Camilla enjoyed the food which Manoel chose for them all. There was the famous green soup that Dennis had told her about, which was basically a potato soup with strips of green cabbage floating in it. This was followed by roast sucking pig and vegetables, which she had never eaten before, and then a large bowl of mixed fruit from which she chose a pear.

'What do you think of our Portuguese cuisine?' Manoel asked her thoughtfully as she stirred a spoonful of sugar into her coffee.

'That was a marvellous meal in any language!' she smiled back at him.

'I enjoyed it too,' Luis chimed in.

'You look half asleep,' his uncle teased him. 'It is late, young man. I think it is time we took you home.'

Luis made a face at him. 'What shall we do tomorrow?' he asked hopefully.

'Tomorrow I'm going to make copies of some of the tiles,' Camilla told him firmly. 'You can help me, if you like?'

79

' I shall begin my painting of you!' he laughed.

Manoel grinned at them both. ' It won't be easy to catch the exact colour of her hair,' he warned Luis. ' Have you thought about that?'

' Honey-coloured,' Luis said.

' And honey-smelling,' Manoel murmured. ' Have you finished? I think there is a ferry just about to go.'

The ferry was almost empty as they made their way back across the river to the Praça do Comércio. Camilla sat as far away from Manoel as she could and congratulated herself on her sensible attitude towards him. She could even make herself look across at him where he was sitting and assess what it was about him that attracted her so strongly when he was near. There was something about the strong line of his jaw, she decided, and his air of knowing exactly what he wanted. It was romantic to think about the strength in his body and how easily he could overpower her if he chose, but they were qualities that would soon annoy her if she had to live with them. He would be forever telling her what to do, and she needed no man to tell her that!

By the time the ferry had come alongside the Praça do Comércio jetty, she felt quite jaunty and well able to cope with any outrageous remarks Manoel might care to make. It was a kind of teasing, she supposed, and not very different from the compliments any number of men had given her at home. She had been silly to attach any importance to his flirting with her. He probably flirted as easily with any woman under the age of eighty-five! Even, she told herself ruthlessly, dismissing the peculiar feeling of depression the idea gave her, even with the Countess Victoria!

Luis went straight to bed. He gave Camilla a sleepy kiss on her cheek, keeping one watchful eye on his uncle. ' Goodnight,' he said.

' Goodnight yourself,' Camilla answered him. ' Shall

I look in later on?'

Luis nodded, pleased. ' But I shan't stay awake,' he said. ' You won't mind, will you?'

' No, I won't mind.'

Manoel looked from one to the other of them. ' I hope that doesn't mean that you are going to make me drink my brandy on my own?' he asked Camilla lazily.

She gave Luis a last hug. At that moment, she thought with glee, Manoel looked no more dangerous than his nephew.

' Not if you don't want me to,' she replied coolly.

His eyes lit up, but he said nothing to dispel her new confidence. ' I dislike drinking alone,' he told her.

She was surprised. ' I should have thought you'd have liked your own society,' she said gaily.

' I prefer your company.'

She gave him a startled look. ' Manoel—?'

' If you look at me like that, I shall definitely not be able to resist temptation,' he said, smiling.

Camilla wished that she had gone to bed. ' I—I thought you were going to have a brandy,' she said.

' Will you have one?' he asked her.

She shook her head. ' I had more than enough wine at dinner.' She sat awkwardly on the edge of the sofa, pretending not to be aware of him as he poured himself a glass of brandy and came and stood beside her, twirling the amber-coloured liquid thoughtfully in one hand.

' Camilla—'

She jumped nervously and blushed.

' Aren't you being a little ridiculous about this?' he asked her with such charm that she very nearly agreed with him.

' I—I think I'll go to bed after all!'

He sat down beside her, putting his brandy down on the table in front of him. He took her hand in his own and smiled at her.

'Does it frighten you so much when a man kisses you?'

'Of course not! I'm not *frightened* at all! I don't like being kissed by all and sundry, that's all!'

He pulled her close to him and his lips came down on hers whether she would or no. She put up her hands to push him away, but his only response was to hold her closer still. She had never been kissed like this before. It was unbearably exciting. Her lips parted beneath his and she uttered a sound of sheer happiness as her arms slipped up round the back of his neck, giving him kiss for kiss.

'Oh, Manoel,' she whispered.

## CHAPTER VI

'Oh, Manoel,' she whispered.

He let her go. 'Am I the first man ever to have kissed you?' he asked very gently.

She felt warm and flushed. 'I—I— *L-like that!*' she admitted.

His eyes teased her. 'Where has the ice-maiden gone?'

'That isn't very kind,' she said with dignity.

'No, perhaps it wasn't. If you knew what a challenge that cool, unapproachable you is to any man—'

'Don't!'

Manoel drew her close again. 'Why are you so afraid of being hurt?' he asked her.

'Oh, but I'm not!' she denied. 'I wouldn't like to hurt anyone else, though,' she added. 'N-not like that!'

'Like what?'

His voice sounded warm and lazy and she barely noticed his fingers in her hair, removing the pins that held her hair in place.

' I would never *play* with anyone!' she said fiercely.

' Do you think I am playing with you?'

' I don't know,' she said.

Her hair fell in a cloud to her shoulders and she made an ineffectual attempt to push it back behind one ear.

' Life is for living,' he said lightly. ' Being hurt is better than not living at all.'

' You wouldn't say that if you had seen—' She broke off, afraid of being disloyal to her mother.

' I shall try not to hurt you, my darling,' he promised. ' But you don't make it very easy for me. I want you, my love, and I think that you want me!'

She gazed at him in startled outrage. ' Oh, but—' she began, and blushed. ' I haven't thought about it.'

' Then think now,' he invited her. His arms went round her and he began to kiss her again, ignoring her protests. His body felt hard against hers and the exploring caress of his hands aroused her emotions as nothing ever had in the past.

' You see how easy it is?' he laughed at her.

' Too easy!' she retorted.

His lips came down on hers, silencing her, and she held him closer still, responding to his embrace with every part of her being. He murmured something in Portuguese, pulling gently on her hair. Then as suddenly he released her and stood up.

' It is too soon to decide what we are going to do about this,' he said abruptly. ' You must see this. It is as well that the maid is sleeping in your room, my dear, don't you think?'

' There's nothing to decide!' she gulped.

He gave her an arrogant look. ' Nothing? What is your solution?'

Camilla shook her head. She knew how very vulnerable she was. He had walked into her life, unasked, and had smashed her carefully erected defences against this very situation, and now he thought that she would agree to anything he suggested, but she was made of sterner stuff than that!

' I shall go back to England,' she sniffed. ' Luis doesn't really need me. It won't be long before Denis and Leonor come home.'

' That would solve nothing,' said Manoel.

' It would for me!'

' You will do as you are told! You cannot hide behind that business of yours for ever! We will send for your mother—'

' I won't see her!' Camilla informed him, very agitated.

' You have need of your mother at this time,' he frowned at her. ' She will chaperone you—'

Camilla laughed hysterically. ' My *mother*?'

' She is the obvious person,' he said haughtily.

' She is more likely to compete with Dona Victoria to be your duchess!' Camilla retorted.

Manoel's expression changed to one of distaste. ' We are speaking of your mother, Camilla,' he reminded her sternly.

She sighed. ' I don't think you know my mother very well,' she said gently.

' She is still your mother.'

Camilla shivered. ' I don't want her to be! I don't want to see her! I want nothing to do with her, just as she wants to have nothing to do with me!'

Manoel took her hands in his. ' Are you quite sure that that is true?' he almost pleaded with her.

' Quite true. You've never lived with her—I have.'

' But, my love, no one is as bad as you make her out to be. She has a right to be with her daughter at this moment in her life. I wish to get to know every member of your family.'

' Why?' she asked him blankly. She was ashamed,

84

but she didn't want to argue with Manoel. She didn't even want to talk to him. She wanted him to kiss her again—to feel again the delicious tumult of feeling that his touch aroused in her. To discuss her mother at such a time was like a douche of cold water in her face.

'I want to know everything about you,' he told her. 'Is that so strange?'

'No,' she said. Then, 'Yes. It's unnecessary!'

'How can you say that?' he demanded.

She attempted a laugh. 'I'm not so silly as to think that you haven't kissed a great many women—'

'That is no business of yours!'

She threaded her fingers together nervously. 'I—I know,' she conceded. 'But you couldn't possibly have wanted to know all about the families of all of them!'

'Camilla! Do you never think before you speak? Let me tell you that it is not at all attractive for you to discuss such matters with me!'

She was quite suddenly furiously angry. 'You forget that I am not one of your Portuguese dependents! I'm used to saying what I think—'

'And a great deal too used to having your own way,' he finished for her grimly. 'No wonder your mother washed her hands of you!'

'Let's leave my mother out of this!' she retorted.

'That is no longer possible. Tell me about her, Camilla?'

She stood up hastily, almost tripping over her own feet. 'No! Why should I? My mother isn't any of your business—'

His hands gripped her shoulders so tightly that he hurt her. 'And what about you? Are you also no business of mine?'

What answer she would have made, she never knew, for his hands slid down her arms to her wrists and, clipping her hands behind her back, he kissed her angrily

85

on the mouth. For a moment she resisted him, but she needed his kiss as much as he needed her, and she could fight him no longer.

'Well?' he asked her, almost as if he hated her.

'In—in a way,' she admitted.

He shook his head at her. 'Stubborn to the last?' he said with a smile.

Even such a small glimpse of affection upset her and she began to cry, brushing the tears away from her cheeks with the back of her hands.

'I'm not stubborn,' she said. 'Not really—'

'Then tell me about your mother!'

'I can't while you're disliking me,' she sobbed.

'*Disliking* you!' he exclaimed. 'You have an odd way of expressing yourself, my love. I am liking you a great deal too well!'

She put her face against his shoulder and cried in earnest. 'I-I'm sorry,' she said at last. 'I *never* cry!'

'Just as you never kiss?'

'It doesn't agree with me!' she went on pathetically. 'I look awful when I've been crying.'

'You look rather sweet to me—and very young.' He gave her a little shake and kissed both her damp cheeks, seating her firmly back on the sofa.

'I'm not sweet,' she announced in a funny, choking voice. 'None of the Armstrongs are sweet.'

He looked amused. 'My dear, I hesitate to disagree with you, but I find you very sweet indeed.'

'Well, I'm not!' she said forthrightly. 'Sweet women are no good at business, and I make a great deal of money. I'm very successful, Manoel! It won't last, no fashion ever does, but while it does, I intend to become as rich as possible.'

He laughed out loud at that. 'Darling! Is that the whole sum of your ambition?'

'What's wrong with it?' she demanded, genuinely

puzzled.

He laughed again. 'Money will not keep you warm at night!'

She flushed. 'It's more reliable than—than other things,' she ended tamely.

'Meaning men?'

'Well—yes,' she admitted.

'And me in particular?'

Camilla bit her lip painfully. 'I—I wouldn't rely on you for that,' she told him carefully. 'I wouldn't expect it.'

He gave her a long, thoughtful look. 'I think we have come back to your mother, haven't we?' he said.

'I suppose so,' she agreed nervously. 'You should ask Dennis about her.'

'I'm asking you,' he said firmly.

'Dennis is supposed to be more like our father,' she said inconsequentially. 'I don't remember what he looked like—'

'He is dead?' Manoel interrupted her.

'I don't think so,' she answered gravely. 'I think he just—went away.' She saw Manoel's mouth tighten and knew that she would never be able to make him understand how she felt about her mother. 'We're that sort of family!' she added inadequately.

'What sort of family?'

'W-we go away. We're *irresponsible*!' she exploded desperately.

Manoel frowned at her. 'Perhaps if you began at the beginning,' he suggested with considerable charm, 'I might refrain from jumping to the same sort of disastrous conclusions that you are apt to draw about other people!' He leaned forward and kissed the tip of her nose, smiling at her indignant expression.

'I don't think you ought to kiss me,' she reproved him.

87

'I'll kiss you as often as I please!'

She blushed, enjoying, even while she couldn't approve, his air of mastery.

'Dennis thinks our father found another woman and went away with her,' she confided, 'but we don't really know what happened. We heard a lot of gossip, of course, even as children, but I didn't believe all of it.'

'And your mother?'

Camilla hesitated, trying to be just. 'I was too young to know how she took it then, later she was far too busy to have much feeling for anybody or anything!'

'Just like her daughter?' Manoel suggested.

Camilla wished that she could deny it. 'I'm like her to look at, I may be like her in character too.'

'Would that be such a tragedy?'

She was silent for a long moment. 'I think it would be,' she said then. She forced herself to look at him. 'Manoel, you don't have our sort of family in Portugal—'

'No, we don't,' he agreed promptly. 'Our families are very large, with masses of children and therefore lots of aunts and uncles as well as parents and grandparents. We all support one another in everything we do. Did you have no other relations apart from your parents?'

Camilla was surprised to discover that she didn't really know. 'I think there was only my mother,' she said vaguely.

'A young woman, left on her own with two young children, is an object for sympathy rather than disparagement,' he commented quietly.

'I knew you wouldn't understand,' she sighed.

'What did your mother do to make you dislike her?' he asked quietly.

'I don't dislike her!' she denied quickly, too quickly. 'I preferred not to live with her. She—she hates to be lonely, so she always has a great many people around her. She's like the proverbial sailor with a wife in every port,' she added bitterly.

' She is promiscuous?'

Camilla stiffened. 'You've met her,' she said. ' What did you think of her?'

' I thought her a beautiful woman—and an unhappy one,' he answered.

' *Unhappy? Mother?*'

' She was gay on the surface,' he said. ' But underneath? I am not so sure. I think she is more generous than her daughter with her emotions—'

' She hurts a great many people!' Camilla cut in.

' Perhaps they hurt her?'

Camilla lifted her chin proudly. 'You have to like people to allow them to hurt you. My mother doesn't like people. She falls a little bit in love with almost everyone, just enough to make it exciting for her to come and go, to kiss this one here and that one there. If other people are foolish enough to fall in love with her, she finds it amusing and passes happily on to other, greener pastures somewhere else. I don't think she has a single friend whom she has known for longer than a few weeks. I may have been born like her, but if I have any choice in the matter, I shall never *be* like her!'

His arms fell away from her. ' I find it unattractive to speak of one's parent in such a manner,' he said sternly.

' I didn't want to,' she pleaded with him. ' I wouldn't have said anything if you hadn't asked me.'

' But you feel it inside you—'

' One can't help what one feels,' she pointed out.

He frowned disapprovingly. ' What does your mother live on?' he asked.

Camilla shrugged. ' I don't know. Dennis and I send her money sometimes, but she has plenty of her own. She couldn't travel round as she does if she hadn't.'

'You send her money?' he repeated.

Camilla smiled sadly. 'I can't quite hate her, you see—'

'You have told me nothing that makes me change my mind about inviting her here,' he interrupted her curtly. 'How old were you when you went to London?'

'Seventeen.'

'And she allowed you to go?'

Camilla gave him a resentful look. 'It was partly her idea.'

'That I cannot believe!'

'Oh, believe what you like!' she retorted aggressively. 'But Mother doesn't like competition—'

He smiled suddenly. 'And her beaux began to prefer you?' he suggested in amused tones.

'They were *awful*!'

His eyes lit with laughter. 'I cannot bring myself to blame them, somehow.' His amusement died slowly away. 'When you see your mother again you will probably wonder why it was that you disliked her. Can't you bring yourself to believe that?'

She shook her head. 'I don't understand why she has to come,' she told him.

'The Ferrado family has seen enough scandal in recent years,' he said dryly. 'I prefer not to be the one to add fuel to the fire of the gossips.'

She thought then that she understood only too well. The Duke of Ferrado would marry the Countess Victoria in his own time, just as he would do everything else that was expected from one in his position. Meanwhile, he would amuse himself with someone who pleased him better. In the Portuguese way, he would take a mistress and he would give her everything but his name. He would even put up with his mistress's mother!

'But, Manoel—' she protested.

'*Now* do you understand?' he demanded, smiling at

her.

She licked her lips and nodded her head. He took a step towards her and she thought he was going to kiss her again, but that she couldn't allow. If he touched her again, she knew she would be undone. She would be prepared to go to him on any terms, even knowing that he would eventually marry somebody else. But she also knew that in the cold light of day she would want more than that, and she would go back to England and would do her best to forget all about him. For the one lesson that her mother had succeeded in teaching her was that any relationship between a man and a woman that was less than marriage ended in degradation for the woman.

Camilla turned on her heel and ran out of the room, up the stairs and into her room. She forgot that she was not alone and, throwing herself on to the bed in the dark, she wept bitterly.

In the middle of the night, Camilla turned over sleepily and was quite suddenly wide awake. From a placid dream of elegantly clad models floating before her eyes, she found herself in a flat panic and knew that she had fallen in love and that nothing would ever be quite the same again.

She lay awake in the darkness, marvelling that she had ever thought that she would be immune to such a flood of emotion. She had thought that her business was enough for her. It *had been* enough for her! Only now, she knew, that it was not enough and never would be again. She wanted Manoel so much that it hurt. The extraordinary thing was that she had never thought that it could happen to her. And now she would be lonely all her life, because she had known a Portuguese duke, and he had kissed her because she had honey-coloured hair and a cool exterior that had intrigued him. It was obvious, even to her, that such qualifications were not enough for him to think of making her his duchess. That honour was reserved for the Condessa Victoria Arrabida. Camilla conjured up the tight, sour features of the Dona Victoria and wondered how Manoel could bring himself to do it. For a moment she thought that she hated the other woman, and then she realised that she didn't. If anything, she felt sorry for her, for Manoel might marry her and make her the mother of his children, but she knew quite certainly that the Portuguese woman would never, never win his love.

She turned her pillow angrily, punching it into a better shape. It seemed to her that she and Dona Victoria had a lot in common, for Manoel had made it impossible for either of them to be truly happy for as long as they lived.

Camilla breakfasted alone. She had hardly finished her cup of coffee when Manoel's manservant came softly up behind her chair.

'The Dona Joana Arrabida is waiting to see you in the sitting room,' he said apologetically. 'She has another person with her, an acquaintance of her daughter's, whom she is anxious for you to meet.'

Camilla's hand went straight to her hair. 'They want to see me?' she asked in surprise.

'The Dona Joana is a very pleasant lady,' the manservant reassured her. 'In *O Duque's* father's day, she stayed frequently at one or other of the Ferrado houses.'

'I suppose her daughter was with her?' Camilla said more to herself than to him.

'Mostly,' the man confirmed quietly. He held the door for her, plainly intimating that she should not keep the older woman waiting. 'Shall I announce you, *senhorita?*'

Camilla shook her head. She didn't like to say that

92

she was not accustomed to such formality, but she liked Dona Joana and she was sure that the Portuguese woman would think no less of her for behaving naturally. Even so, she took the opportunity to glance at herself in one of the long looking-glasses in the hall to check on her appearance before she entered the sitting room.

' *Minha senhora,*' she greeted Dona Joana in warmly welcoming tones. ' How nice of you to come and see me!'

Dona Joana stood up and kissed Camilla warmly on both cheeks, a decidedly mischievous expression on her face.

' My dear, I couldn't wait!' she said in her perfect English. ' I ran into this young man in the street and I brought him along with me. Allow me to present him to you. Senhor Henri Rodriguez, Miss Armstrong.' Her smile grew wider. ' Senhor Rodriguez sometimes escorts my daughter when Manoel is too busy.'

Camilla found herself looking at a stocky, dark young man, no taller than herself. He wore several gold rings on his hands and his teeth, too, had been stopped with gold, giving a mildly opulent look to his smile. When her eyes met his, she discovered that he had been assessing her with a frankness that embarrassed her. She hoped she had not been staring at him in quite the same way and the thought made her blush.

' You didn't tell me how beautiful your young friend is,' Senhor Rodriguez accused Dona Joana. ' No wonder Dona Victoria didn't wish to accompany you!'

Camilla gave him a quelling look. ' H-how is your daughter?' she asked, trying not to laugh.

Dona Joana managed to look maliciously triumphant and more than a little amused. ' Victoria has a headache,' she said bluntly. ' She is given to them, you know, especially if things are not going well for her.'

' Oh,' said Camilla.

'As a matter of fact, I am here at her bidding,' the older woman went on in amused tones. 'My daughter is very concerned at your position here. She wonders if it is quite *comme il faut* for you to be here at all. She cannot help feeling that it would be better if you stayed in some other house—'

'I agree with her there!' Camilla said with deep feeling.

'Really?' Doña Joana sounded astonished. 'Because of Manoel?'

The ready colour slid up into Camilla's cheeks. 'In a way,' she admitted. 'It's more because I didn't want to come in the first place. I—I worry about how things are going at home.'

'You have a fiancé in England?'

'No,' Camilla said. 'No, nothing like that. I have a design business and I ought to be working on our new collection.'

Doña Joana dismissed this with a magnificent lack of interest. 'I hope you are not thinking of leaving us quite yet?' she said sharply.

Camilla hung her head. 'I promised my brother I'd stay with Luis until he and Leonor get back,' she admitted.

'And that will be when?'

'I'm not sure,' Camilla said uncomfortably. 'Dennis wants to have Leonor to himself for as long as possible.' Her voice faded away, as she noticed that the Doña Joana was looking positively smug. 'I—I don't think he entirely understands what being a Ferrado means. I mean, Luis being a Ferrado,' she stammered on.

Doña Joana looked both sympathetic and interested. 'Didn't you know about Manoel's interest in his nephew?'

'No,' Camilla said baldly. 'Dennis thought—we both thought—that Leonor's husband had been completely cut off by his family.'

Dona Joana nodded with complete understanding.
'The old Duke was very angry about the whole affair.
He would have nothing more to do with Jaime and I
think he would have cut him out of his will if he could
have done so, but the estate is entailed. Manoel refused
to follow the old man's example. As soon as he came
into the title he began to make arrangements for Luis to
take up his father's share of the estate. He saw the
boy whenever he could and made sure that Leonor had
an allowance that was compatible with her position as
Jaime's widow.'

'I can't understand why Dennis knew nothing of this,'
Camilla put in in a small hurt voice.

Dona Joana shrugged. 'That I cannot tell you,' she
said firmly. 'Perhaps she had her reasons. I think
your brother found it romantic that she was a *fado* singer
and a fishwife, earning her own living. It would have
been less easy for her to have remarried had she been
accepted as Jaime Ferrado's widow.' She smiled easily.
'*I* have never remarried, as you can see!'

'Did you want to?' Camilla asked her before she could
stop herself.

'I too could have been the Duchess of Ferrado,' Dona
Joana said dryly. 'I flatter myself that I had more
chance than my daughter!'

Camilla felt herself blushing again. 'Manoel could
hardly marry anyone more suitable,' she said carefully.

Dona Joana chuckled. 'It may amaze you,' she confided, 'but I am extremely attached to my prickly
daughter. She may have ambitions to be a duchess, but
I have an ambition that she will be happy, and she will
never be that with Manoel. So,' she continued happily,
'I have come to deliver her message, but I shall also
do all that I can to encourage you to stay here. Do you
understand me?'

'I—I think so.'

'Victoria thinks it will be much better if you stay with us while you are in Lisbon,' she went on in the same tones. 'What do you think of that?'

'I'd prefer to go back to London,' Camilla confessed.

'But that would never do!' Senhor Rodriguez exclaimed. 'Now that I have seen you, *senhorita*, it is imperative that you remain here!'

'Certainly!' Dona Joana chimed in. 'You cannot run away to London now!'

'W-why not? Surely it would be simpler for everyone?'

'Lisbon would be desolated!' Senhor Rodriguez smiled at her. 'I should be desolated!'

Dona Joana frowned at them both. 'We should all be sorry, but that is quite beside the point! What is necessary is that you should divert Manoel's attention from Victoria for long enough for her to find where her happiness lies. That is not a great deal to ask, surely?'

Camilla found herself laughing. 'I don't know that I want to divert Manoel's attention from your daughter. Whom he marries is no business of mine!'

'Very proper!' the Portuguese woman congratulated her. 'But not very practical. Are you really so averse to catching Manoel's eye?'

'I think,' Senhor Rodriguez put in, 'that I am on the Senhorita Camilla's side in this! Why should Manoel have such an advantage over the rest of us?'

'Be quiet, you!' Dona Joana rapped at him. 'It will be in your interest as much as anyone else's. There is only one thing to be decided between us. Camilla must have a proper chaperone while she is here. I will speak to Manoel about it and then I can tell Victoria that everything is arranged and that your reputation is suitably guarded.'

Camilla felt an excited astonishment within her. This

96

was the most ridiculous conversation she had ever had with anyone. The thought of anyone diverting Manoel from his chosen course made her want to laugh. Yet it was a temptation not to go back to England, but to stay in Lisbon and let these extraordinary people take charge of the future. Supposing, just supposing, that Manoel really wanted her? She didn't believe it for a moment, of course, but if the Countess Victoria were to be married to another—?

Camilla felt herself blushing, but she looked bravely straight into the laughing eyes of Dona Joana.

'As a matter of fact,' she began, with a slight catch to her voice, 'Manoel is asking my mother to come to Lisbon to be with me while Dennis and Leonor are away. He—he thought it would be nice for us both.'

Dona Joana flung up her hands in triumph. 'Splendid! Absolutely splendid! I can't wait to tell Victoria that!'


CHAPTER VII

The advent of Camilla's mother found favour with everyone except Camilla. She told herself that she was older and more mature than the last time she had confronted her parent face to face, but as her coming drew nearer, so did Camilla's confidence ebb away almost to vanishing point.

Happily, the visit to Luis's estate in the country took place on the Thursday before Mrs Armstrong was due to make her appearance, and Camilla was able to forget for a few hours at least that her mother was coming and that she was somehow going to have to come to terms with her.

The day out had something of a holiday atmosphere about it. Manoel came down to breakfast dressed in casual clothes. He was much taller than most Portuguese men and he wore his clothes well. It would have suited Camilla's comfort very much better if he had been more ordinary, she thought grudgingly. As it was, her heart lifted at his appearance and it was as much as she could do not to make her appreciation obvious to him and anyone else who was looking at her.

'We have a fine day for the trip,' Manoel said cheerfully. He grinned across the table at his nephew, who had already had his breakfast upstairs, but had come to talk to Camilla while she had hers. 'You will have to decide for yourself if I am looking after your tenants well,' he said sternly. 'It is time you grew to love your own land.'

'Yes, Tio,' Luis said submissively.

'Your father was much loved by his people,' Manoel remembered. 'He had the knack of making everyone like him. When we were boys, I was a little jealous of him because he could make friends so easily.'

Camilla started. 'But you—' she began.

His amused glance met hers. 'I don't make friends easily,' he said. 'My mother used to tell me that I have an arrogant manner that puts people off until they get to know me.'

'That's true!' Camilla said with feeling.

'I thought you might agree,' he said smugly.

She eyed him thoughtfully. 'Mmm. I can't imagine you singing for your supper in a *fado* house!'

'You malign me! I have done that often in the past!'

She could almost believe it, when she saw him dressed as he was today. Almost, but not quite!

'Did you go with your brother?' she asked him.

'Sometimes,' he said abruptly. He frowned suddenly and deliberately changed the subject. 'We will take a packed lunch and have a picnic. Luis, will you please go and tell Carlota? We will be starting in about half an hour.'

The boy went immediately, excited by the thought of having a picnic in the country. Manoel looked after him, his eyes sad. 'He is young to be introduced to his responsibilities.'

'I quite agree,' Camilla said heartily. 'I should have thought it would be soon enough when he was grown up.'

But Manoel shook his head. 'The life he leads with his mother is no preparation for the kind of demands that will be made upon him when he is older.'

'His life will be different now,' Camilla pointed out coolly.

Manoel lifted his eyebrows. 'From what?' he demanded.

Camilla gave him a resentful look. 'We live quite a respectable life in London, you know,' she retorted crossly.

'*Very* respectable, I have no doubt,' he drawled.

'Well, we are! There's little time for anything else besides work—'

'And little inclination?' he suggested.

'I wouldn't say that!' she denied sulkily.

His eyes lit with laughter. 'At least there was no time for you to grow into a woman. For that you can thank Portugal!'

She refused to answer him. 'Are you sure you wouldn't rather take Luis on his own?' she asked instead.

'I wouldn't dream of it, my dear,' he answered dryly.

'I don't think I want to go,' she added.

He laughed aloud. 'You'll enjoy yourself, Camilla, I promise you that. It is our last day of freedom, have you remembered that? Tomorrow your mother will be here and how often will we be alone together after that?'

'We shall have Luis with us today,' she reminded

99

him, determined to be awkward.

His grin was arrogant and, to her, quite unbearable.
'Does that worry you?' he enquired lazily.

'No,' she answered tautly. But it did worry her.
She didn't want to be alone with Manoel and Luis was
easily diverted. She didn't trust herself. She sighed
heavily. It was strange that with disaster staring her in
the face, she seemed quite incapable of changing the
course of events as she always had in the past. Manoel
wasn't the kind of man that one could lightly side-step,
she reflected miserably. Manoel was the kind who made
the running and those about him had little choice but
to follow where he led. And *that* bothered her! Any
running that was to be done, she wanted to do herself!

'Poor Camilla!' Manoel drawled.

She blushed. 'Why?' she faltered.

He put a hand on her shoulder, making her jump.
'You're so sure that your independence is the most
important thing you have.'

She lifted her chin. 'So it is!' she said hotly.

'Poor Camilla!' he said again.

He strolled round the table, still laughing at her, kissed
her lightly on the mouth, and sauntered out of the room.
Camilla sat, staring at her plate for a long moment, her
fists clenched in her lap. She would, she decided, be
glad to see her mother after all. Most of all she longed
for Dennis and Leonor to come home and release her
from her imprisonment in Manoel's house. All she
wanted was to get back to London and her work, and
to be herself again.

Manoel brought the car round to the door himself,
hurrying everyone into action as the car blocked up most
of the narrow street. Carlota hurried out, carrying an
enormous picnic basket which he put in the back seat,
ordering Luis to get in beside it.

Camilla stood in the doorway, refusing to look at anything but the tiny cobbles that made up the dazzling white pavement outside.

'Come on!' Manoel bade her.

'I'd rather sit in the back,' she objected.

But Manoel wasn't listening. He wrenched open the door, caught her by the hand and pushed her into the car in one easy movement.

'You're looking very pretty!' he congratulated her. 'Is that dress one of your designs?'

She nodded, blinking the tears out of her eyes. 'L-Luis likes it,' she told him.

'Playing for safety again?' he teased her.

'Not playing at all!' she retorted dryly.

He laughed delightedly. 'I shall have to see what I can do to change your mind about that—'

'You won't!' she snapped.

His laughter unsettled her. 'We have the whole day in front of us,' he reminded her. 'Shall we forget our differences until tonight?'

She glanced at him warily, suspecting some kind of a trap, but his smile was enough to dissolve her worst suspicions, and she found herself smiling back at him.

'All right,' she agreed carefully. Then she relaxed suddenly and chuckled. 'Can you forget that you're a duke for a whole day?' she asked him.

'Is that part of the deal?'

'Isn't it?' she demanded sharply.

'If you'll forget all about your wretched independence?'

She chewed thoughtfully on her lower lip. 'I don't think I can,' she said. 'It—it isn't something you can pick up and put down at will.'

'Like being a duke,' he said smugly. 'Shall we just agree not to fight?'

'Oh yes!' she agreed with relief. 'It's too nice a day, and tomorrow—' She broke off, unwilling to remind either herself or him that her mother would be there.

'Tomorrow is another day,' he said gently.

Camilla nodded and managed a casual smile. 'Perhaps it won't come,' she said flippantly.

'At least it won't be as bad as you think,' he answered with complete certainty.


Lisbon was looking particularly pretty. A light breeze was just sufficient to make the waters of the Tagus dance beside the solid, pleasing architecture of the Marquês de Pombal, who had rebuilt Lisbon after the devastation of the earthquake when practically the whole city had lain in ruins. Everywhere were the same white pavements, sometimes patterned with black basalt, and always beautiful. They were suitably narrow and crowded in the smart shopping areas, widening out into calm, long stretches beside the tree-lined avenues that converged on the famous round 'square' of the Praça Marquês de Pombal, whose agricultural and shipping interests are recorded at the foot of the obelisk erected to his memory on the central island.

Traditional Lisbon soon lay behind them. The new residential areas were clean and spacious, marred only by the chaos that followed the line of the extension to the underground system which was still in the process of being built. Manoel pointed out the airport to her, adding that one day it was hoped to move it to the southern side of the river.

A few miles of motorway took them rapidly out of the suburbs of the city, along beside the river and the occasional industrial estate.

'Is this where they float the port in special boats down to Lisbon?' she asked dreamily.

'The boats come down from Oporto,' he confirmed. 'But it is too late in the year to see them now.'

It was not too late to see some of the wine-producing vineyards however. The grapes had been picked long since, but the vines were now scarlet with age and ready to shed their leaves on to the equally red soil. The land looked rich and productive and, every now and again, Manoel would point into the distance and tell her that he had lands in this or that direction.

'You seem to own the whole of Portugal,' she said at last.

'Not quite,' he said modestly. 'Luis, too, owns quite a large piece.'

'All Ferrado land,' she murmured. It frightened her a little to think how many people must work for the Ferrados in one way or another. It seemed to her as though his lands stretched endlessly out between them, keeping them apart. No wonder he wouldn't consider marriage with her, she thought. Camilla Enterprises seemed small and rather pointless alongside the centuries of history that lay behind the Ferrado name.

'You mustn't allow it to frighten you,' he responded. 'One must love the land, but one must always remain its master.' He smiled briefly. 'Land is rather like a beautiful woman. It has to be husbanded to give of its best.'

Camilla felt quite shattered by such a comment. 'That involves a commitment, not a passing relationship,' she said bracingly.

'Isn't that the best way?'

'I think so,' she said. 'It doesn't sound very Portuguese.'

'That is because you still don't understand us very well. First one chooses the land and then one loves it. You, I think, would prefer to do things the other way round?'

It seemed they were back to the Condessa Victoria with a vengeance!

'I think I'd prefer not to be loved—or married—
because I was *suitable*,' she averred.

Manoel only smiled.

'It's—it's cold-blooded!' she rushed on, in the face of
his silence.

'I don't think you are in much danger,' he said
kindly.

'What? Of being married?' She was furiously
angry.

'Of being married for your suitability,' he returned
smoothly.

She swallowed. 'Why? Am I so unsuitable?' she
asked, hurt to the quick. Did he too consider Camilla
Enterprises to be too small to be of any consequence?

'You're too pretty for any man's comfort!'

'And that makes me unsuitable?' she pressed him.

'N-no.'

'Then—then why?'

'I can think of other reasons for marrying you,' he
said at last, his voice tinged with arrogance.

Why, he's shy! she thought with a flash of intuition.
The knowledge went to her head like wine.

'Really?' she said with anxious curiosity.

'It must have something to do with your honey-
coloured hair!' he conceded. 'Beautiful land is not
always the best for husbandry, however,' he added
crushingly.

'Just to possess?' she suggested.

He gave her a quick look. 'To have and to hold,' he
said thoughtfully. 'That is what makes land desirable.
It wouldn't go with your independent nature!'

'I suppose you like your women submissive—and
dull!' she said grandly.

'Why should you object?' he drawled.

'Because I shall never submit to any man!' she
retorted harshly. 'I'm—I'm not ambitious that way!'

He whistled softly. 'But you do have a barbed tongue, my love!'

'I d-didn't mean anyone in particular,' she assured him hastily.

'Your meaning is perfectly clear,' he told her. 'Victoria is noble in her own right. She has no need of my name to add lustre to hers.'

'Of course not,' Camilla said with open dislike. 'Portugal *is* a republic these days.'

'For the last fifty years,' he agreed dryly.

'To me,' she said, 'Leonor's ancestry is far more interesting. Her family go back for just as long as yours! I expect one of them sailed in one of Vasco da Gama's ships too, if one only knew!'

'Very likely,' he agreed easily.

'So Leonor is just as good as Victoria!' Camilla went on provocatively.

'I wouldn't dream of denying it,' he answered. 'You're quite jealous enough as it is!'

She gave him an outraged look. 'I am not!'

'Then you shouldn't flirt with someone whom you obviously believe to be another woman's property.'

'I don't flirt!' she gasped.

'My dear girl, you flirt with every breath you draw!'

'I do not!'

His eyebrows rose dramatically. 'If it weren't for our truce, I'd make you tell the truth about that,' he smiled at her.

Camilla retired into a dignified silence. They had left the wine-growing district now and the road ran between closely planted trees belonging to the forestry commission. Many of the trees were eucalyptus, their shedded bark lying in a heap at their feet as if they were discarded clothes not yet kicked off. The smell of the trees added a sharp tang to the air. Camilla shut her eyes, drawing pictures in her mind of dresses made from materials in the silvers, greeny-browns, and bright yellows of the spindly trunks. They would be exactly right for the coming winter, she thought. She would call the whole collection ' Eucalyptus Forest '. Coming after the Lisbon tiles, it would be exactly right.

' What are you thinking about now in that golden head of yours?' Manoel asked her.

' Colours.'

' Colours?' he repeated.

' They're very important,' she said gravely. ' To my job!'

' Oh yes?'

' Yes. I don't own half Portugal, but Camilla Enterprises is important to me!' she told him roundly.

' And to quite a number of other people, I should imagine,' he agreed.

' You—you don't think it unimportant, then?' she almost pleaded with him.

He looked startled. ' Why should I?' He frowned. ' Do I really have to tell you how much I admire you for building up such a venture?'

' But—' she began.

' We don't understand one another very well, do we?' he said with charm. ' Why should you think that your work is unimportant to me?'

' You don't like my independence,' she said bluntly.

' That is something quite different!'

' I don't see how it can be!' she sighed.

' You could not design successfully unless you had the freedom to do so,' he explained gently. ' That is quite different from how you are in your relationship to the man in your life.'

' I don't see how you can separate the two,' she objected.

' It is difficult,' he admitted. ' Perhaps it is particularly difficult for a woman. It's understood that a man will earn his living and yet be the man in his own household, but not yet that a woman may work and still be a wife and as such subject to the man.'

'Why should she be subject to anyone?' Camilla wondered.

'Would you rather that your husband was subject to you?' he countered.

'No,' Camilla admitted.

Manoel shrugged his shoulders. 'You are fortunate,' he told her. 'You could design just as easily at home and send your work to Dennis in London—'

'And be at the beck and call of my husband?' she put in indignantly.

'That would have to be seen to be believed!' he laughed at her.

'I don't think Dennis could manage—' she began. She stopped, blushing, wishing she had kept her mouth shut.

'No, he has always clung to your apron strings. It would probably be the best thing for him.'

'You don't know him!' Camilla accused him.

'No, I don't,' he admitted. 'I know only what Leonor has told me. You smother him, Camilla, whether you want to or not. Leonor wants me to find a job for him here in Portugal.'

'I don't believe you!'

'You don't have to,' he said grimly. 'When they get back, I shall make up my own mind about him and act accordingly.'

'I shall never forgive you if you take Dennis away from me,' she told him bitterly, her voice trembling in spite of herself.

He looked across at her and smiled. 'It will be Dennis's own decision,' he promised her. 'Are you unsure of him?'

'No, of course not!' she exclaimed, relieved. Dennis

would never leave Camilla Enterprises. It was as much his creation as hers—in a way. 'Dennis has always worked with me,' she added. 'We rely on one another for everything!'

'But now he has Leonor and Luis,' Manoel reminded her. 'It would be better for them if he didn't rely on you quite so much.'

'Because you don't like him working for a woman?' she accused him.

'Not for you,' he answered firmly. 'He is a man, not a little boy for you to mother! If you want to indulge your maternal instincts, you'd do better to marry and have children of your own!'

She looked out of the window, seeing only her own tears. 'I haven't much chance of that either, if you are to be believed!' she hit out at him.

'Not if you plan to run your husband as you do your business!' he answered cheerfully. 'If he allows you to do so!'

'I'm sure if you had your way I'd be sufficiently cowed to obey his every wish!' she said sarcastically. 'There are times, duke, when I find it quite easy to hate you!'

'I should be disappointed if you didn't!'

Camilla sagged a little. She didn't understand a word he had said. Why should he presume to advise her about her affairs? Good, healthy anger made her feel a little more cheerful.

'You don't know anything about Camilla Enterprises,' she said quietly. 'When I want your advice about how I run my business, I'll ask you for it. I'm sure Victoria would be charmed to receive your views on anything and everything, but I happen to like to think for myself!'

'And for Dennis too?' he asked unkindly.

'What he does in Camilla Enterprises is my business!'

she retorted.

'And what he does with his life with Leonor is mine!' he returned coolly. 'Nor do your constant references to Victoria please me. It is easy to see that whatever else your mother did for you, she certainly exercised no control over your tongue or your manners!'

'The pot calling the kettle black!' Camilla suggested contemptuously. 'You've done nothing but criticise me ever since you first saw me!'

'There is so much to criticise,' he drawled.

'I hate you!' she assured him for the second time.

'If you did, you would hardly come picnicking with me in the country,' he said arrogantly. 'Don't be silly, Camilla.'

She turned her back on him and stared out of the window. They were approaching a small town, she noticed, and wondered what it was. There was a great deal of building going on beside the road. Here and there were dotted about piles of the Continental type of biscuit bricks waiting for the builders to cement them into rough walls, which were easy to plaster and easy to keep cool in the long, hot summers.

'Are we near the *quinta*?' Luis asked excitedly from the back seat, rubbing his eyes sleepily.

'Fairly near,' his uncle replied. 'There is a church here that I want Camilla to see.'

'Why?' the boy demanded.

Manoel grinned. 'That's a surprise. If you come closer, I'll tell you.' He slowed the car while Luis leaned forward, putting his ear against his uncle's lips.

Camilla tried to hear what he said, but she could not. She put her elbow on the arm-rest in the door of the car and pretended that she didn't care what secrets they had between themselves.

Luis giggled happily and returned to the back seat, his eyes dancing. 'After we've seen the church, we'll be going to the *quinta*,' he told himself, squirming with pleasure. ' And after the *quinta*, we are going to Nazaré. It will be very late when we get home!'

Manoel drove the car into the centre of the small town and parked it neatly in the shade of a tree.

' Welcome to Caldas da Rainha,' he said briefly to Camilla. She thought he still sounded disapproving and she sniffed sulkily to show him that she wasn't exactly pleased with him.

' It's a very funny name,' Luis said buoyantly. ' The Baths of the Queen,' he translated. ' Which Queen, Tio? Why did they belong to her?'

' Queen Leonor,' Manoel said, laughing a little. ' She saw some peasants bathing in some evil-smelling water and asked them why they did so. They told her that the water was very good for rheumatism and she decided to try it herself there and then, although she was on her way to her father-in-law's funeral. She had hardly left the place before she began to feel the good effects, so she came straight back here and turned it into a spa. The church was built at her behest.'

' Queen Leonor?' Camilla repeated with relish.

' Leonor is a very popular Portuguese name,' he said with amusement.

They went in to the fifteenth-century church, which was situated just to the left of the spa buildings. Camilla covered her head with a scarf from her handbag, though none of the other women inside had anything over their heads, so she was a moment or two behind the other two in seeing the full glory of the interior. She recognised the Manoeline style decorations round a fine pair of Gothic windows, but this was a mere detail, for the whole of the walls were covered with fine seventeenth-century *azulejos*, or tiles, and better still were the altar frontals with Moorish sixteenth-century *azulejos* in relief. Camilla paused, stunned by the magnificent display.

'They're *beautiful*!' she exclaimed.

Manoel nodded, well satisfied. ' I think they are some of the most lovely in the country. I thought you might find them inspiring,' he added with humour.

She cast an ecstatic look round the church, reaching automatically into her handbag for her sketching pad and a pencil. With delight, she began to copy some of the designs, gaining her effect with a few confident lines on the page. Then she hesitated, and looked thoughtfully over to where Manoel was standing. Why should he encourage her by showing this magnificence, she wondered, if he didn't approve of her work or the way she went about it? He stood below a Manoeline type of triumphal arch, hand in hand with Luis, staring upwards at the fine Crucifixion above. Looking at him, Camilla could feel her heart begin to thud and a wave of emotion swept over her, making her hands tremble. What was she to do? Distracted, she tried to concentrate on her brief sketches of the *azulejos*, drawing wildly on page after page.

In a few minutes Manoel came over to her, glancing over her shoulder at what she was doing. Camilla felt him stiffen and looked down herself at what she was doing. A strong face looked back at her out of the page, instantly recognisable. It was Manoel.

Shutting the sketching block with a bang, Camilla subsided into the nearest pew, her knees too weak to support her.

' I-I— It needed a figure to give the size of the arch,' she stammered by way of explanation.

' Which arch?' Manoel asked, smiling faintly.

' I haven't put it in yet,' she said.

He took the block from her protesting fingers and began to look through it, coming inexorably back to the drawing of himself.

' Do I really look like that?' he asked, holding it this

way and that.

'Like what?' she asked hollowly.

'So—unyielding,' he said.

'Yes, you do!' she informed him eagerly. 'You never give in at all! You're arrogant, conceited, stubborn, and invariably sure that you're right about everything! And I dislike you very much!'

Manoel went on looking at her drawing of him, the faint smile on his lips growing broader at every word.

'You dislike—this man?' he enquired, pushing the drawing under her nose with the very ruthlessness of which she was accusing him.

'Yes. *Yes!*' she repeated.

'Oh, Camilla,' he said, so gently that she was almost beguiled into looking up at him, 'don't you ever tell the truth?'


CHAPTER VIII

The gateway to the *quinta* was a tall, ornate archway in the middle of nowhere. On the top was a statue of St Louis, looking towards the horizon, beyond which lay Tunisia, the country in which he died.

'Is that because of me?' Luis asked, well pleased with his first sight of his own estate.

'Your grandfather was a Luis too,' Manoel told him.

Luis's face took on a set expression. 'He didn't like Mama,' he said.

'He didn't give himself a chance to find out,' Manoel reasoned casually. 'He was an old man.'

'I suppose you liked him,' Luis said with a sigh. 'Was he your father?'

'That's right.'

'Then why was he such an old man? You're not very old, are you?'

'He married very late in life,' Manoel said briefly.

'Did he know your mama for a long time?' Luis persisted.

'Yes, he did.'

'Then why didn't he marry her sooner?'

Camilla managed a faint smile. 'He was probably wondering if she was sufficiently suitable,' she observed.

Manoel's hands clenched on the steering-wheel. 'My mother was very much younger than he was,' he said in controlled tones. 'She had a weak heart from birth and she died soon after Jaime was born.'

'I'm sorry,' Camilla said inadequately.

'It was the conclusion that I knew you would jump to,' he replied unpleasantly. '*And* give voice to!'

Camilla bit her lip. It seemed that she could do nothing right. 'Do you remember her at all?' she asked him.

'A little.'

'I have seen a picture of her,' Luis put in proudly. 'Papa showed it to me once. It is in a museum, isn't it, Tio?'

'Yes,' his uncle said, dismissing the subject of his mother. He pointed into the distance. 'The house is over there. At the moment it is empty, but there is a woman who goes in to keep it clean and so on. Perhaps, one day, you'll live in the house yourself?' His smile was very gentle as he looked at his nephew.

'Is it—*my* house?' Luis asked thoughtfully.

'Absolutely.'

'Then why doesn't Mama live in it?'

'She is married to an Englishman,' Manoel explained. 'She will want to live in England with him.'

Luis swallowed painfully. 'Do I have to live in England?'

'Some of the time,' his uncle said. 'Some of the time you can live with me, if you like?'

' Here?'

' We will visit here, but I usually live in Lisbon or in one of my other houses. I have to see to my own estates as well as yours.'

' I see,' said Luis. He sat with his arms propped up on the front seat, looking at everything as they drove slowly onwards towards the house. ' Do I own any more houses?'

' Two more,' Manoel told him. ' You have one in the Algarve that the family has always used for their holidays, and one quite close to Oporto.'

' Don't I have a house in Lisbon?'

' No. I own the Lisbon house. I am giving your mother her house in the Alfama, for her wedding present. It has been in her family for many years.'

' Yes,' Luis confirmed. ' It's a nice house, but I prefer your house.'

Manoel grinned at him. ' Why? Because it's grander?'

Luis shook his head. ' It's more private,' he said gravely. ' Everyone is always coming in and out of Mama's house. They sing very loudly all night long and I can't get to sleep.'

' I prefer your mother's house,' Camilla chimed in.

' Naturally,' said Manoel.

She turned her head away to hide the hurt he had dealt her. ' It's smaller,' she explained in a small voice. ' I'm not accustomed to having servants in the house.'

' Only at work?' Manoel suggested mockingly.

' Not there either.'

His smile taunted her. ' Are you trying to tell me that you are domesticated and feminine about the house?'

' No,' she said bleakly. ' I'm not trying to tell you anything. You'd only twist whatever I said to suit yourself!'

' Would I now? I wonder why?'

'Because you're beastly—'

'Tio is beastly?' Luis asked her, much interested.

'Only sometimes,' she conceded ungraciously.

'Are you cross with him?' Luis demanded.

'She's *very* cross with me,' Manoel chuckled.

'Why?'

'I caught her out in telling a lie,' Manoel explained solemnly.

Luis looked shocked. 'Mama gets cross when I tell a lie,' he told Camilla sternly.

'This was the unvarnished, unpalatable truth!' Camilla claimed doggedly. Her eye was caught by Manoel's and she blushed. 'It was true!' she insisted.

Manoel glanced at his nephew. 'Do you think she dislikes me?' he asked him.

Luis shook his head positively. 'You only kiss people you like,' he said unanswerably. 'And she kissed you, didn't she? If she didn't have to work, she'd think about marrying you.' He sighed sadly. 'Only she hasn't got time,' he confided knowledgeably.

'Is that so?' Manoel drawled.

Camilla uttered an agitated sound and strove vainly to look amused, blasé, and coolly sophisticated.

'You said so, didn't you, Camilla?' the small boy said complacently.

'N-not exactly,' she muttered.

'It sounds an interesting conversation,' Manoel put in helpfully.

'I said I didn't want to marry *anyone*!' Camilla said fiercely.

'Because she has to work,' Luis nodded triumphantly. 'I told her you wouldn't make her work, and that being English it wouldn't matter that she isn't a Condessa.'

'But I knew better!' Camilla added with a slightly hysterical laugh.

To her surprise Manoel threw back his head and roared

with laughter. 'I should hope you would!' he said to her.

'You'd make me—darn your socks!'

He laughed some more. 'I'd sit back and let you earn enough for both of us!' he teased her. 'Designing clothes, the girl calls it! Drawing portraits of dukes, *and* without their permission!'

Camilla sniffed. 'I don't have to ask your permission for *anything*!' she exclaimed in hunted tones.

'Not yet!' he retorted.

To Camilla's relief they drew up outside a very pretty pink house, with bright green shutters, and curling pillars on either side of the front door.

'This is my house! Mine!' Luis said with deep pleasure. 'I think it's the prettiest house I've ever seen!'

'Definitely!' Camilla agreed with a smile.

Manoel got out of the car and opened Camilla's door for her, watching her closely as she stepped out on to the drive, her face alight with pleasure and interest.

'Your hair is coming down,' he told her conspiratorially.

She put a hand up quickly, feeling the pins that held her hair in place. It was as firmly in position as it ever was.

'Oh, you!' she said crossly.

'Why don't you do a self-portrait some day?' he asked her, his eyes crinkling in the corners in a way that made her unaccountably breathless.

'I—I don't think so.'

'Have you never tried to paint? I fancy an oils of you. I shall have to think who would be the best man for the job.'

Camilla took a deep breath. 'I don't think I want to sit for a portrait,' she told him flatly.

'But you've told me one doesn't have to ask the

sitter's permission,' he reminded her casually.

She glared at him. ' I wouldn't fit in with your illustrious ancestors!' she said tautly.

Manoel fingered her hair lightly. ' My mother—' He broke off, changing his mind. ' Why don't you want to be painted?' he asked instead.

Camilla trembled beneath his touch. ' One has to consider the feelings of other people,' she answered him frankly. ' I know how I'd feel—' Her voice caught in her throat. ' H-hadn't we better go into the house?'

He frowned. ' Very well,' he agreed politely. He stood aside and allowed her to precede him up the few steps to the front door. Luis was already there before them, hammering on the door with his closed fist.

' Is there anyone inside?' he asked plaintively.

The door opened before Manoel could answer him and a small, button-eyed woman smiled a welcome to them all. She dropped a small curtsey to Manoel, kissed Luis firmly on both cheeks, and held out a work-worn hand to Camilla, laughing and talking all the while.

' Entre, minha senhora!' she bade Camilla warmly.

' Senhorita,' Manoel corrected her quietly.

The button eyes travelled from one face to the other with obvious interest. ' Senhorita? I hope you find the young senhor's quinta pleasing to you. Are you staying for lunch? Can I get you a cup of coffee?'

Camilla brought out one of her carefully learned polite phrases. ' Não se incomode, por favor,' she said gently.

' Ah!' the woman exclaimed meaningly. ' You are already learning to speak Portuguese! O Duque is teaching you, I expect?'

' Well, no,' Camilla denied uncomfortably. ' He speaks English so well that I am apt to forget that it's not his first language.'

Manoel grinned at her. ' Perhaps you would understand me better if I talked to you in Portuguese?'

'Do I misunderstand you?' she countered.

'Often,' he stated firmly. 'Whether wilfully or not, I have yet to make up my mind.'

'Perhaps you don't make your meaning very clear,' she said quietly. 'I understand what you say, but not always why you say it!'

He smiled at her, glancing towards the housekeeper in a warning gesture. 'My meaning is as plain as the nose on your face! It's your own response that's in doubt.' He took Luis by the hand and led him into the house, bending over the boy to hear what he was saying. 'Of course we shall see everything while we are here. You must meet all the workers as well.'

'Yes, of course,' Luis agreed. He went on excitedly in Portuguese, marvelling over everything that he saw. Camilla, watching the two Ferrados, felt out of place and wondered what was expected of her.

'You—you won't want me with you,' she said hurriedly. 'I'd like to have a look round on my own. You don't mind, do you?'

Manoel gave her a kind look that brought the colour burning into her cheeks. 'Thank you,' he said simply. 'Luis would be better alone while he is meeting his tenants and getting to know the place. We'll meet back here for lunch in about two hours—will that suit you?'

Camilla nodded quickly. The relief of being alone was a joy to her. She felt as though she had shed a great weight and was feeling the autumn sunshine for the first time on her skin. She walked as fast as she could away from the house, down a long avenue of trees towards a formal garden in the distance. It was a beautiful day and she was in love. Love was a painful emotion, jagged and demanding, but just for the moment Camilla was determined to glory in the ecstatic dither to which Manoel could reduce her with a single look. It was a love that was destined to lead nowhere, unless she was prepared to throw all her carefully nurtured principles straight out the window, but it wasn't ended yet. She felt again the feel of his lips against hers and the touch of his fingers on her hands and her hair. She had never suspected that love could be like that, an all-consuming passion that went to the depths of her being. Her mother's loves were light and frequent. She could almost envy her, for she knew quite certainly that Manoel would hold her whole heart for ever, even if she were never to see him again.

She sat on a seat, facing the sun, and shut her eyes, conjuring up Manoel's face in her mind's eye. She felt deliciously lazy and soft inside. With a smile, she put a hand up to her hair and unpinned it, shaking her head to free the cloud of honey-coloured hair about her shoulders.

The moment she had done so, she regretted it. How was she going to put it up again without a looking-glass? The housekeeper would think her a fine fool! And Manoel? But she preferred not to imagine his comments, or the look in his eye—

'*Senhorita*, what a pleasant surprise!'

Camilla opened her eyes and stared into the face of Senhor Rodriguez.

'What are you doing here?' she asked, not at all pleased at being discovered at such a disadvantage.

'What are you?' he returned easily. He sat down on the seat beside her, appraising her with his bright eyes.

She sat up very straight, pushing her hair back behind her ears. 'The *quinta* belongs to Luis,' she explained briefly.

'So it does. I had forgotten that this was Jaime's share of the estate. Of course Manoel can afford to be generous.'

Camilla looked at him sharply. 'What do you mean? If this was Jaime's land, it's obvious that Luis would inherit it from him.'

'But it was never actually Jaime's,' Senhor Rodriguez drawled. 'Jaime died some time before his father. The old Duke cut him and his family out entirely. Manoel had no need to hand the *quinta* over to Luis.'

Camilla frowned. 'He had a moral obligation!'

Senhor Rodriguez laughed. 'That doesn't always count for much!'

'It depends on the people concerned, *senhor*!' Camilla said with dignity.

Senhor Rodriguez shrugged, smiling into her eyes. 'My name is Henri, won't you call me that?'

'If you want me to.' She wished he would go away, but she was too polite to say so. 'You haven't said what you are doing here?' she reminded him.

'The Condessa Victoria's estate lies just over there,' he explained. 'It has long been her ambition to add this *quinta* to the rest.'

'Luis's *quinta*?'

'The old Duke was prepared to sell it to her for a nominal price. It is understood that sooner or later she will marry Manoel and then her estate will go to the second son. This *quinta* runs better with her lands than with the Ferrado estate.'

Camilla gasped. 'And what has that to do with you?' she demanded.

Henri Rodriguez laughed softly. 'Everything the Dona Victoria does is my business.'

Camilla puzzled over this in silence for a minute, then: 'Are you related to her?' she asked.

'Heaven forbid!' he exclaimed forcibly.

'Then—'

He smiled, his gold teeth flashing in the sunlight. 'You are delightfully innocent, my dear. And very, very attractive!' He touched her hair, laughing when she pulled away from him. 'Manoel is a lucky man!'

Camilla's eyes widened in shock. 'I don't understand what you mean!' she disclaimed.

'No?' His eyes gleamed as brightly as his teeth. 'An arranged marriage is an unromantic business. You and I are not important enough to figure in such an affair, but there are compensations. The Dona Victoria is inclined to be kind, providing one is discreet—'

'I think it's horrible!' Camilla burst out.

He laughed. 'Why is it all right for you, but not for me?' he asked her.

'I didn't say that!' she denied indignantly.

His laughter died away and he regarded her with astonishment. 'Forgive me,' he said. 'I think I have misunderstood your position?'

'I think you have!' she agreed dryly.

'I can only apologise. But tell me, what did you make of Dona Joana's visit the other morning?'

Camilla stirred uncomfortably. 'What should I have made of it?' she demanded crossly.

'Dona Joana was the victim of an arranged marriage,' he told her. 'She is fond of Victoria, and has no intention that she shall make the same mistake—'

'I gathered *that*!' Camilla said wearily.

Henri Rodriguez shrugged his shoulders. 'Victoria is a very ambitious woman, but she can't force Manoel to ask her to marry him.'

Camilla allowed the silence to grow between them. If she were wise, she thought, she would change the conversation to something less personal. She didn't like to feel that she was discussing Manoel's private affairs behind his back.

'Where do you come in?' she asked abruptly.

His smile was back and his eyes were bright again. 'I mean to marry Victoria myself,' he told her. 'You see, I too have my ambitions.'

Camilla could scarcely stop herself from laughing.

'You want to marry *Victoria*?' she repeated.

He shared her amusement. 'Why not? A plain woman is grateful for a man's attentions. She will give me a free hand, you know. It will not be a bad life.'

'Poor Victoria!' Camilla said with feeling.

'Have you no ambitions?' he asked defensively.

'I keep mine for my work,' she said coolly.

He shook his head at her. 'That's no way for a beautiful woman like you to be! You could have a great many men at your feet if you chose.'

'I don't choose!' she snapped at him.

His gold teeth shone brightly. 'I don't believe you've ever tried! Hasn't Manoel even kissed you?'

'That's none of your business!'

'I see he has! Did you dislike it? Of course not! No one could attract and promise so much and give only a little. How beautiful you are, Camilla, with your lovely hair!'

Camilla stood up with resolution. 'I dislike personal remarks, *senhor*,' she said coldly.

He smiled up at her. 'No woman objects to being told she is beautiful!' he accused her.

Camilla walked away from him. She felt cold inside and wished urgently that she hadn't been such a fool as to unpin her hair. She shivered and quickened her steps, but she was too late. Henri's hands clamped down on her shoulders and he turned her to face him.

'A little kiss is not much between friends,' he murmured.

'Then why don't you kiss Victoria?' she demanded furiously.

He made a wry face. 'That is duty,' he said frankly. 'This—this is ambrosia!'

Camilla struggled against him, cross with him and furious with herself. His lips were soft and disgusting to her.

'Let me go!' she said when she could, more irate than hurt.

'It's only a little bit of fun,' he laughed at her. 'Why don't you let yourself enjoy it?'

'Enjoy it?' she exclaimed. 'I hate it!'

But he only laughed again, determined to kiss her once more. Camilla rejected him violently, pushing him away from her as hard as she could. He was too strong for her, however, and his arms went round her again, holding her hard against him whether she would or not.

Then just as suddenly she was free.

'Go up to the house, Camilla,' Manoel bade her in tight, angry tones.

But her legs wouldn't work and the anger she had felt dissolved into tears that ran down her cheeks and dripped through her fingers.

'Oh, Manoel!' she sobbed.

Without a thought, she walked straight into his arms, resting her head against his shoulder and crying as if her heart would break. She heard the two men talking as if in a dream, conscious only of the safe, hard feel of Manoel's comforting arms. She felt his fingers combing her hair and, finally, he gave it an angry tug.

'Go up to the house,' he repeated. 'I'll speak to you later.'

'But—' she began.

She could feel his laughter and was oddly reassured. 'Go on, Camilla!' He laughed again. 'I don't know about your heart, but at least your instincts are sound!'

'M-my instincts?'

He put a hand under her chin and forced her to look at him. His eyes were angry and accusing, even while he smiled. 'You came to me like a homing pigeon. But why, Camilla?'

'Why what?' she asked, trying to wipe away her tears.

He wrenched at her hair again. 'Perhaps you are more like your mother than I thought,' he said bleakly.

'*No!*'

He gave her a push in the direction of the house. She walked, half stumbling between the trees, breathing deeply to stop the sobs that tore at her. Now that she didn't have Manoel's comforting presence to reassure her, she felt sick. She leaned against one of the trees to give herself time to recover, and still the tears came, coursing down her cheeks as if they would never stop.

It wasn't long before Manoel caught up with her. He pulled her hands away from her face and towed her after him towards the house, ignoring her ineffectual pleas that she could walk by herself.

'Oh, Manoel, please!' she moaned. 'I can't face Luis like this!'

He came to an abrupt stop, his angry eyes resting on the top of her head.

'You'd better do up your hair,' he suggested.

'I can't find the pins!' she sobbed.

In the end, he did it for her, mercilessly jabbing the hairpins into her scalp. 'What inducement did he offer you?' he asked in wintry tones.

'He didn't.'

Manoel's eyebrows rose in disbelief. 'Did you know he was going to be here?'

'How could I have known?' she sighed.

He looked at her in silence. 'Then why, Camilla?'

She avoided his eyes, chewing at her lower lip. 'We —we were talking,' she said.

'*Talking?* What did he say to make you loosen your hair?'

'That was before,' she swallowed. 'It was the sun and—and everything. And then he came. I asked him what he was doing there.'

'That's easily answered,' Manoel said. 'He often

gives Victoria a hand with her estates.'

'And you don't mind?' she asked before she had thought.

He shrugged. 'Her estates are nothing to do with me.'

Camilla blinked at him, her tears forgotten. 'He was horrible,' she said with distaste. 'I—I had forgotten—'

His hand closed round her wrist, so tightly that it hurt. 'I keep telling you, Camilla, that you are not in England now. Have you no sense? What did you say to him to make him think that you wanted his kisses?'

'Nothing!' she denied vigorously.

'I don't suppose you had to,' he admitted crossly. 'The look of you is enough to tempt any man.'

'Don't!' she pleaded.

'Then tell me what it was that you had forgotten?'

She hung her head. 'You wouldn't understand!' Her eyes met his briefly. 'I'd forgotten how dirty it makes one feel to be kissed—like that,' she told him proudly.

His grip on her wrist tightened until she cried out. 'I really believe that you think that you can walk through life unscathed, without taking the slightest precaution to ward off the Henris of this world. You don't know what you do to a man, with that hair of yours all round your shoulders, and that shy, sweet look in your eyes!'

'But I didn't *do* anything!' she protested.

He kissed her hard on the mouth. 'You didn't have to,' he conceded. 'Thank goodness your mother is coming to look after you tomorrow!'

Camilla sighed. 'Where's Luis?' she asked inconsequentially.

'He's looking at the horses.' Manoel grinned at her.

'Shouldn't you be with him?' Camilla asked anxiously.

'I thought I'd come and see what you were up to,'

he said. ' Just as well I did! I thought I'd find you busy sketching something or other,' he added basely, his lips quirking with amusement.

She shook her head. ' No, I wanted time to think,' she said.

He laughed out loud. ' Are you sure that's wise? No good ever came out of a woman thinking?'

' I suppose you'd rather I was confused for ever,' she answered without rancour.

' Are you confused?' he asked, intrigued.

' A little,' she managed. She rubbed her wrist thoughtfully, exploring the small bruises his fingers had left there. ' To be honest,' she added with a little laugh, ' I don't know if I'm standing on my head or my heels!'

Camilla glanced at her face in the looking-glass as she smothered her nose with powder to hide the tell-tale stains of her tears. She looked, she thought, remarkably normal when she considered her fraught experiences of the morning. Only she knew that she had finally made up her mind. It wasn't only that Dona Victoria wasn't in love with Manoel, she didn't deserve him either. Anyone who could compare Henri's kisses with those of Manoel, who could even prefer Henri's kisses, must be mad!

Camilla felt very sane and quite, quite sober. She knew that Manoel would never marry her, but she thought that she could be content with very little. It would be enough, she told herself, to have loved him as a woman must love a man. She would accept any terms he cared to offer her, and she would regret nothing. There was nothing else that she could do. Yesterday she might have gone back to England. Today she hadn't got the strength to leave him. She would stay until he sent her away.

# CHAPTER IX

Camilla's mother arrived earlier than anyone had antici-
pated. She stepped out of the taxi and, waving a
languid hand in the direction of Manoel's manservant,
said clearly, ' Pay him, someone, would you? I don't
seem to have the right currency on me.'

She wouldn't have, of course, Camilla thought. But
she did have enough luggage with her to have brought
every garment she possessed. The pile of suitcases in
the hall grew steadily under Mrs Armstrong's watchful
eye, until she had counted the right number of pieces,
when she turned at last to greet her daughter.

' Well, Camilla?' she said.

' Hullo, Mother,' Camilla responded, equally cool.

Mrs Armstrong looked about her and smiled slowly.
' Not bad, darling. Not bad at all! Where's Dennis?'

Camilla felt embarrassed. ' I thought you knew,' she
said. ' Dennis is married. That's what I'm doing here.'

' I don't see how I could know,' her mother responded,
' seeing that neither of you see fit to tell me anything.'

' No,' Camilla admitted. ' I'm—I'm sorry,' she
added.

Mrs Armstrong favoured her with a long, cool look.
' I was in London last week,' she said. ' I called in at
Camilla Enterprises and got a whole new wardrobe while
I was there. You're doing very well, darling.'

Camilla sighed. ' My clothes are mostly for the
younger woman,' she observed.

' Ouch!' said her mother. ' I thought you'd like me
to look the well-dressed mother of the famous designer
daughter. I also thought you'd be glad to know that
the whole place hasn't collapsed while you've been
away.'

'I didn't imagine that it would,' Camilla said with a confidence she was far from feeling. 'I suppose you charged the clothes to my account?'

Her mother chuckled. 'No, to Dennis's,' she said calmly. 'It was his turn—' She broke off as she caught sight of Manoel coming down the stairs towards her. 'Is *that* the attraction, darling? Who'd ever have thought it of you, Camilla?'

Camilla cleared her throat, determined not to allow her mother to paralyse her with embarrassment as she had so often in the past. 'Mother,' she said in a voice not quite her own, 'I should like to present you to our host, the Duke of Ferrado.' A smile touched her lips as she felt her mother's shock at her words and she wondered if she should, after all, have presented Manoel to her. It was too late now. 'This is—my mother,' she ended lamely.

Manoel bowed politely over her mother's hand. 'It was kind of you to visit us at such short notice, Mrs Armstrong. I expect you would like to see your room? I will ring for Carlota to take you to it. Afterwards, I hope you will have some coffee with us in the sitting room?'

'Us?' Mrs Armstrong enquired maliciously.

'My nephew and myself,' Manoel returned calmly. 'Your daughter has decided to work in the mornings and we are careful not to interrupt her if we can help it.'

Camilla's jaw dropped, but she pulled herself together with an effort. 'I'll come upstairs with you, Mother,' she offered.

Carlota led the way up the stairs, her skirts rustling. Mrs Armstrong, preening herself in the looking-glasses and ignoring the magnificent *azulejos* on the walls, went next. Camilla, slow-footed and half hoping that Manoel would call her back, followed on, hating herself that she couldn't be more pleased to see her mother.

Carlota paused on the first landing. 'Your daughter's room is in here, *senhora*. *O Duque* wished that she should be near the child. I hope you will not object to another flight of stairs?'

Mrs Armstrong gave Camilla a meaning look. 'Close to the child, or close to the man?' she asked in an audible whisper.

Carlota's skirts rustled disapprovingly. 'The *senhorita* has a maid sleeping in her room,' she said stiffly. '*O Duque* himself insisted on the arrangement.'

'Bad luck, darling,' Mrs Armstrong said casually.

Camilla merely looked sulky. 'Mother!' she reproved.

Mrs Armstrong laughed. 'Oh dear,' she said, 'I see your sense of humour is as inadequate as ever. You'll have to learn to laugh at life sooner or later, or it will get you down.'

'Perhaps we laugh at different things,' Camilla said patiently.

'Very likely!' her mother observed. 'I take it the Duke is *not* a subject for mirth?'

'No.'

'Well, that's definite enough,' her mother chuckled. She stepped into the bedroom that Carlota had prepared for her. 'What a charming room!' she exclaimed. 'Thank you *so* much—Carlota, isn't it? What pretty flowers! You have gone to a lot of trouble! I do hope I am not going to be a nuisance to you.'

'It is never a trouble to carry out the wishes of le *Duque*,' Carlota retorted. 'Please tell me if there is anything further you require.'

The housekeeper set off down the stairs again without a backward look, her head held high and her skirts rustling more frantically than ever.

'I don't think she took to me,' Mrs Armstrong complained. 'And I was trying so hard! Oh, well, I expect I'll find the Duke easier to manage. Men are always more amenable than women, don't you find?'

'I haven't thought about it.'

'No, you wouldn't,' her mother said promptly. 'As prim and proper as ever, aren't you? I suppose you still rule Dennis every waking moment? Poor lad, he never could call his soul his own!'

Camilla froze. 'What do you mean?'

'Oh, lord!' her mother said. 'I swore I wouldn't quarrel with you too! Not until I found out what was going on, anyway,' she added with a flash of self-mockery. 'What should I mean? Dennis has always relied on you to do his thinking for him! You know that, surely?'

'No, I didn't,' Camilla said bitterly.

'You and the ostrich! I suppose you approved his wife before he married?'

Camilla blinked. 'I'd never met her until the day before the wedding.'

'Really? Good for Dennis!'

'I like her very much!' Camilla added defensively.

'Perhaps I will too—when I meet her,' Mrs Armstrong said dryly.

Camilla recognised the familiar feeling of being put in the wrong that she had always associated with her mother. 'You move about such a lot, I expect Dennis didn't know where you were,' she said uncomfortably, wishing that she didn't sound so apologetic.

'It's a nice thought!'

Camilla tried hard not to feel guilty. 'Don't you think we ought to be going downstairs?' she suggested.

But her mother was in no hurry. She sat down on the edge of the bed, crossing her legs elegantly in front of her.

'I intend to hear all about this duke of yours first,' she announced calmly.

'He isn't mine!' Camilla protested.

Her mother chuckled. 'But are you his, darling?'

Camilla blushed scarlet. She had known exactly how it would be, she thought desperately. Somehow or other, her mother made everything seem shoddy, just as she always had.

'No, I'm not!' she snapped.

Her mother eyed her shrewdly. 'But you'd like to be! How well I know the feeling! And where do I come in?'

'Nowhere,' her daughter retorted frankly. 'It was Manoel's idea to ask you to come to Lisbon, not mine!'

'Manoel? How nice! I see you are much more familiar with the Duke than you pretended to be downstairs!'

'I don't wish to discuss it!' Camilla whispered.

'No, you wouldn't,' her mother agreed objectively. 'I suppose you're busy pretending to yourself that you don't want him to ask you to marry him?'

Camilla shook her head. 'He's going to marry the Condessa Victoria Arrabida,' she said abruptly.

Her mother's eyebrows rose. 'I think I remember her,' she said, surprised at her own feat of memory. 'Come to think of it, I saw her dancing with the Duke last time I was in Lisbon. I don't think I was introduced to either of them, though, I was rather taken up at the time.'

'Naturally,' Camilla said nastily.

'A cold-looking woman with greedy eyes,' her mother went on, just as if she hadn't spoken. 'I remember thinking it was a pity to waste such a nice name on her. She had a mother in attendance who never danced at all!'

'I expect she felt that her dancing days were over when her husband died,' Camilla put in.

Her mother chuckled appreciatively. 'Darling!' she protested. 'I really believe you're trying to be nasty!

How fortunate that I find I don't mind in the least! I was beginning to think you hadn't changed at all, but there is a certain something about you that I don't remember. You've become quite human!'

Camilla restrained a laugh. 'Wasn't I human?'

'No, dear, you were not! You were too good to be true, disapproving of everything I did and making me feel like some kind of monster. I was actually *glad* when you took the bit between your teeth and departed for London. I made a small effort to keep Dennis with me, but you soon scotched that—'

'*I* did?' Camilla said, astonished.

'Well, perhaps you didn't,' her mother conceded. 'It doesn't matter now.'

'It certainly isn't how I remember it,' Camilla said flatly.

Her mother had the grace to look abashed. 'There was that rather nasty little man who was following me around at the time, but you didn't leave over him, did you?'

'You know I did!'

'Did he bother you? I seem to remember he had a taste for young girls.'

'He had,' Camilla agreed dryly.

'So you vanished virtuously to London?' Mrs Armstrong gave her daughter an all-embracing look. 'You were quite delectable to look at, even at seventeen. One can't blame the man—'

'You didn't,' Camilla reminded her. 'You blamed me!'

'Did I?' Her mother looked thunderstruck. 'I suppose I did have rather a yen for him. It would have been different if you'd suffered from puppy fat, or something like that, but you looked a rather better version of myself, and I found that rather difficult to live with.'

'So you said,' Camilla smiled. 'Amongst other

things.'

Mrs Armstrong bit her lip thoughtfully, shrugging her shoulders. 'Never mind, dear,' she said with magnificent aplomb. 'That's all in the past! Now my darling little daughter has need of me and behold, here I am!'

'How kind of you!' Camilla interposed ironically.

'Well, it is,' her mother objected. 'I was doing very nicely in Vienna and I can't imagine that your duke is going to entertain me at all. He looks at me just as if he thought I dyed my hair!'

'He does,' Camilla couldn't resist telling her.

'Well, so I do,' Mrs Armstrong admitted. 'I suppose you have tiresome ideas about not improving on nature—'

Camilla giggled. 'Camilla Enterprises would fall down and collapse if I thought that!'

'You can afford to be superior,' her mother said with dignity. 'You have the most gorgeous natural colouring. Has this duke of yours told you that yet?'

Camilla trembled inwardly. 'He's commented on the colour of my hair,' she said primly.

'You make it sound so romantic!' her mother said sarcastically. 'If he's not going to marry you, what does he want?'

The colour slowly rolled up into Camilla's cheeks. 'I —I think he has some other arrangement in mind. Apparently that kind of thing is understood in Portugal when a man holds his sort of position.'

'You mean you've agreed to be his *mistress*?'

'Not yet,' Camilla answered steadily.

'But you're going to?'

Camilla's eyes dropped to the floor. 'I d-don't know,' she stammered. She blushed again as she became aware of her mother's astonished gaze.

'And to think I thought you hadn't changed!' Mrs Armstrong groaned, covering her face with her hands.

'Camilla, my love, how are the mighty fallen!'

Luis was only too ready to tell Camilla what Manoel had said to her mother over the coffee cups.

'He was astonished that from the age of seventeen your family had done little or nothing to protect you,' he informed her solemnly. 'Your mother was not entirely pleased.'

'You surprise me,' said Camilla.

Luis grinned. 'Tio said that a gently nurtured girl should not have been left to her own resources no matter what the circumstances!'

Camilla grunted with annoyance. 'And what did my mother say to that?' she asked, trying to look as though she didn't really want to know.

'She asked him if that was why he was offering you something less than marriage,' Luis said blithely, his eyes dancing.

'Luis! You shouldn't have been listening!' Camilla reproved him.

'Tio was very angry,' the boy continued. He had been brought up on gossip in his mother's house and enjoyed it quite as much as any of his elders. 'He said there was a time and place for a woman to learn to hold her tongue!'

'Oh, my mother will have loved that!' Camilla sighed.

'She laughed,' Luis told her in disappointed tones. 'And then he laughed too.'

Camilla put the finishing touch to her design and held it up to the light. 'What do you think?' she asked him, her head on one side.

'Is it for a dress?'

'Doesn't it look for a dress?'

'I suppose so,' he admitted. 'Are you going to wear it?'

'I might,' Camilla said.

'Will it be honey-coloured?'

She laughed. 'It can be any colour. I can make it honey-coloured if you like.'

Luis nodded. 'Like your hair,' he approved. 'Will you send it to London?'

'My hair?' Camilla teased him.

He giggled. 'No, your drawing!' He reached up and touched her hair. 'I don't like your mother's hair. Why does she have it the same colour as yours?'

'It grew that way, I suppose,' Camilla murmured.

'No, it didn't,' he said certainly. 'You can see behind her ears.'

Camilla stared at him. Was it possible? she wondered. An upsurge of sheer amusement caught in her throat. And to think that she had lived with her mother all those years and she had never noticed!

'Oh, Luis!' she said uncertainly.

He gave her a nervous look, expecting her to be angry. 'I won't tell anyone else!' he assured her eagerly. 'Only we three will ever know!'

'That's all right, then,' Camilla said, relieved. 'My mother will never tell!'

'Nor will Tio,' Luis maintained stoutly.

Camilla sat quite still on her chair, burning with indignation. Was nothing about her, or her family, to be allowed to escape Manoel's sharp eyes? And why did every bit of that knowledge have to be so shaming to her? It was a sign of her immaturity, she told herself sternly, that she should want to apologise all the time—
*especially* for her mother! Her mother's charm was well known. She was young for her age, popular, and a laugh a minute. It was quite unreasonable to resent and dislike her more than anyone else she knew, but she did.

Luis gave her a concerned look, still afraid that the sudden gusts of anger that shook all the adults he knew at times should be shared by Camilla too.

' Tio said he hadn't offered you less than marriage,'
he told her in a small voice. ' He said he hadn't offered
you anything at all!'

Camilla stared at him for a long moment, the tears
gathering behind her eyes.

' I suppose he hasn't,' was all she said.

At lunchtime, Mrs Armstrong said she was going to spend
the afternoon in her room. ' It always takes me a day
or so to recover from flying,' she told them all complacently. ' They say it's ridiculous with these splendid
modern aeroplanes, but I can remember a time when
they shook themselves almost to pieces just taking off!'

Manoel had a withdrawn look that secretly dismayed
Camilla. She could feel the rift between them as though
it were a physical reality and when he looked so unapproachable, she was afraid that it would be there for
ever.

' I'll take Luis to the Castelo de São Jorge,' she said.

' Will we go on our feet?' Luis asked immediately.

' I will take you in the car,' Manoel said stiffly. ' I
am going past that way. You will have to find your
own way back, though. I'm not sure when I shall be
home.'

' Thank you very much,' Camilla murmured.

' Not at all,' he said swiftly. ' The pleasure is mine!'

She wished that she could believe him. She hurried
Luis into his coat so as not to keep him waiting and
they stood together on the front doorstep, pretending to
a serenity that neither of them felt.

Manoel left the engine running as they got into the
car. Camilla sat beside him, her fingers nervously pluck-
ing at her skirt. She barely noticed the river as they
sped along beside it, turning off into ancient, narrow
streets that led up to the castle. Manoel drew up underneath the ramparts. He reached out a hand and took

136

both of Camilla's in his, his eyes crinkling into a smile.

'Have a nice afternoon,' he said.

'I will,' she answered coolly. 'I'm going to do a few drawings. I'm getting on quite well with the collection —thanks to your instructions this morning!'

His eyebrows rose. 'I thought you wanted to have some time to yourself to do some work,' he said reasonably.

'So I do!'

'Then what are you complaining about?'

She gave him a quick look and discovered that he was laughing at her. 'I don't know what my mother thought!' she exclaimed.

'But you can guess?' he suggested.

She blushed. 'She's hardly changed at all,' she sighed.

'No,' he agreed. 'I don't suppose she has. She's still a very unhappy woman. Don't let her rile you, my sweet. You might even end up liking her!'

Camilla shuddered. 'Never!'

Manoel laughed shortly. 'Don't be so stubborn, Camilla. You can afford to be generous—'

'Not to her!'

He leaned across and kissed her on the mouth. 'I don't believe *everything* she says, if that's any comfort to you,' he teased her.

Camilla's hair stood on end. 'What has she been saying?' she asked hoarsely.

Manoel grinned. 'What indeed?' he said.

He reached across her and opened the door, signalling for her to get out. She swung her feet down on to the cobbled street and walked away up the path towards the castle without a backward look.

'Tio—?' Luis's voice came clearly up to her.

'*Sim.*'

The rapid exchange of Portuguese was too fast for Camilla to understand any of it. She kicked out at a passing stone and watched it roll down the path towards the car. A second later she was following it, running pell-mell towards Manoel. But she was too late. Luis came dancing up the path towards her, a pleased smile on his face.

' Tio says I am not to annoy you this afternoon,' he shouted out to her.

Camilla watched Manoel's car disappear round the corner of the narrow street. Her heart felt like a stone within her.

' You don't annoy me,' she said gently.

' No, but Tio says—'

' Perhaps he doesn't want you to tell me what he said,' Camilla suggested carefully.

But Luis continued, quite unperturbed, ' Tio says I'm to be very kind to you.'

' Oh?' Camilla said coldly. ' Did he say why?'

The boy nodded enthusiastically. ' He says nobody has ever been very kind to you—'

Camilla scowled at the path ahead of her. ' What a ridiculous thing to say!' she said harshly. ' How does he know? And who does he think he is anyway?'

Luis hopped along beside her happily. ' Tio says—'

' I don't care *what* he says!'

The boy lapsed into silence, making Camilla feel guilty. She glanced down at him apologetically. ' What does he say?' she said on a sigh.

' Tio says that you're beautiful,' he ended. ' I think you are too!'

Camilla smiled at him. ' Thank you, kind sir!'

He ran a few steps ahead of her. ' I'm going to find the guinea-fowl,' he announced. ' There are all sorts of white birds in the gardens here, but the guinea-fowl are the tamest. I can make them eat from my fingers. Shall I show you?'

Camilla had never seen a pure white guinea-fowl

before. They hopped up and down the stone steps in front of her, mixing with the white peahens that strutted back and forth, squawking irritably at one another when anything occurred to annoy them.

' Will you draw them?' Luis pleaded with her.

She smiled and took out her sketching pad, reproducing the birds with a few firm lines on the paper.

' Can I try?' Luis asked her.

She handed him the pad and watched his efforts as he stuck out his tongue in an agony of concentration. ' I wish they'd stand still!' he complained at length.

' They never do,' Camilla told him, ' except when they're sleeping like that one in that tree!'

' It doesn't look right on paper,' Luis said solemnly. ' I think you'd better draw them. You make them look better than I do.'

She accepted the pad and began to show him how to make perspective work for him, but Luis soon grew tired of drawing birds and wanted to try his new skill on something else. Camilla looked about her and saw a shady parapet only a few yards away from them, from where one could look out across the whole city. To her delight she found there was a map of the main buildings made of tiles and she was able to use this to explain in greater detail how to reduce three-dimensional things to two on paper. After a while Luis wandered away, leaving her to doodle to her heart's content, finding inspiration in the curve of the river, the strong red lines of the Salazar bridge, and the embracing arms of the Christ the King on the far side of the river.

They walked home, taking their time as they wandered down towards the river. Luis pointed out the spot where King Carlos and the heir to the throne were assassinated in 1908, giving her a bloodthirsty account of the incident that almost had her believing that he was there in person. Better still, in her opinion, was the ornate fish market, where his mother had still worked sometimes until she had married Dennis.

Camilla knew where she was the minute she saw the carved caravel of the monument to the Explorers.

'We're nearly home!' she encouraged Luis.

He gave her a well satisfied look. 'You are beginning to like Lisbon, no?'

'Yes, I am,' she agreed.

'That's good,' he said briskly. 'Tio says he hopes you will learn to feel completely at home here. Do you think I will like London?'

'I think you will,' she assured him.

He threw his arms out in an expansive, cartwheeling movement. 'I *love* Lisbon. It's the most beautiful city in the world!'

Camilla escorted her mother upstairs to bed with a set expression on her face. For hours they had listened to a racy description of this and that city and every detail of what Mrs Armstrong had done in each one of them. It had been quite different from the evenings that Camilla had spent fencing with Manoel, half hoping that he would kiss her and half hoping that he would not.

'Darling,' her mother's voice said loudly, 'you're going about this in completely the wrong way! I don't suppose for a moment that you will take my advice, but—' She laughed without amusement—'for once I know what I'm talking about, and you have to prod a man into action!'

'I'd sooner be dead!' Camilla growled.

Her mother frowned irritably. 'I am your mother—' she began.

Camilla took a deep breath. 'I know,' she said as gently as she could, 'but I've got used to managing on my own. Please don't try to help me, Mother. I don't want Manoel on those terms.'

'I thought you wanted him on any terms you can get?' her mother retorted.

Camilla blanched. 'I want him on his terms,' she said. She felt rather than saw her mother's astonishment and backed away from her before she could say anything else to cheapen what she felt for Manoel.

'Goodnight, Mother,' she said.

'Here, wait a moment!' Her mother beckoned to her imperiously. 'Is there anything in that library downstairs that I can read? Be a love, and fetch me something in English, will you?'

Camilla turned and retraced her steps down the stairs without a word. She would not have thought of rifling Manoel's library for her own use, but she could think of no good reason for refusing her mother. She had never been in the library by herself before and she had not realised what a fine collection of books Manoel kept there. When she switched on the lights, she saw the long lines of leather-bound volumes and despaired of finding anything that would amuse her mother for the odd few minutes before she slept. She had turned to go when she heard footsteps crossing the hall behind her.

'Manoel!' she called out.

He came into the library. 'I thought you had already retired?' he said.

'My mother wanted something to read,' she explained breathlessly. She thought he looked peculiarly fine in his crimson smoking jacket, and besides, the mere sight of him seemed enough to make her feel weak at the knees.

'You had better come into my study,' he told her. 'I have a few English murder stories in there.' He smiled mockingly. 'I read them when I am pretending to work.'

He switched off the lights, leaving her to stumble after him in the darkness into the brilliantly lit hall. His study was on the other side of the house, a businesslike room, full of masculine gadgets and a small bookcase crammed full of paperbacks in a variety of languages.

'Here you are,' he said, handing her a selection of books.

She took them from him, avoiding the touch of his fingers on hers.

'Are you—are you going to bed now too?' she asked him shyly.

His smile was wintry. 'No, I am going out.'

She was startled into looking at him. 'Going out? Now?'

'In Lisbon our night life begins very late. I have an engagement for supper in a *fado* house. Another night, when your mother has recovered from her journey, we can all go together.'

Camilla clutched the books to her, feeling cold and lonely. 'Are you going with Dona Victoria?' she burst out.

He put his hands on her shoulders, turning her round and propelling her out of the door.

'Your mother is waiting for her books,' he said.

'But are you?' she demanded.

'I believe she is to be one of the party,' he admitted haughtily. He gave her a little shake. 'Satisfied?'

She gave him a frightened look. 'It isn't any of my business.' She made a dash towards the stairs, juggling with the books in her nervousness as she went.

'No, it isn't,' Manoel agreed dryly. 'Goodnight, Camilla.'


CHAPTER X

Camilla went down to breakfast early, but even so Manoel was before her. He stood up as she entered the dining room, greeting her gravely and holding her chair for her as she took her seat.

' Did you have a pleasant evening? ' she couldn't forbear to ask him.

He looked amused. ' I enjoyed it, yes,' he said. ' Dona Joana enquired after you.'

' That was kind of her,' Camilla acknowledged smoothly.

' I told her that you were safely tucked up in bed,' he added with a smile.

' She might believe that you know,' she retorted tartly.

' Perhaps that is why she wishes you to converse with a young female relative of hers. I have agreed that you should do so. It is time you began to perfect your Portuguese.'

Camilla stared at him. ' My Portuguese? '

' We all indulge you in this house by speaking English to you,' he went on imperturbably.

' But I'm not sure that I want to learn Portuguese! ' she protested.

' It will be necessary for you when you open a branch of Camilla Enterprises here in Lisbon,' he explained briefly.

' But—'

' Must we have an argument about it? ' he demanded irritably. ' Isn't it enough that it would please me if you were to learn my language? '

She gasped, hesitating only for an instant. ' Yes,' she said at last, ' it is.'

' Good. Then I shall make the necessary arrangements.'

' Th-thank you.'

His amused glance met hers. ' Well? ' he prompted her.

' I can't imagine why you should think that I am going to open a branch of Camilla Enterprises here? ' she said flatly.

'Well, perhaps not you personally,' he replied. 'I shall talk to Dennis about it some time.' He smiled thoughtfully. 'Leonor is going to be a difficult plant to transplant.'

Camilla felt unaccountably disappointed that it was Dennis that he was considering.

'Dennis doesn't make that sort of decision on his own,' she informed him coolly.

His eyebrows flew up. 'Isn't he to be trusted?'

'Of course he is! Only neither of us make that sort of decision on our own!'

'But this time I think it will be his decision,' Manoel said certainly. 'I can't see that it is of any great interest to you!'

Camilla eyed him stubbornly. '*Everything* to do with Camilla Enterprises is of interest to me,' she reminded him sourly.

'In the past, yes,' he agreed.

Her heart thudded within her. 'It always will be!' she asserted stubbornly.

He reached across the table and took her hand in his. 'Cling to your independence as long as you can, my dear,' he teased her gently. 'It may even help you to bear with your mother for a few days. It has always been your defence against her, hasn't it?'

Her eyes dropped away from his. 'You don't sound as if you approve?'

'I don't!' he said bleakly.

She blushed a little. 'I don't suppose a Portuguese girl would defy her parent under *any* circumstances!' she taunted him.

'She might try,' he admitted.

She managed a wry smile. 'You surprise me!'

'Do I indeed?' He gave her fingers a squeeze. 'You tempt me to say something quite unbecoming about your past life,' he murmured.

But then he didn't have to say that he didn't approve of her, she thought. She knew that as well as she knew her own name. She peeked at him through her eyelashes, searching for the right words.

' If Dennis wants to open a branch in Lisbon, I shan't —shan't object to it, if you don't want me to,' she said at last.

His eyes smiled right into hers. ' I didn't think you would,' he said smugly.

She reclaimed her hand from his, annoyed with herself for making it so obvious that she wanted nothing better than to please him. She bit her lip until it hurt.

' Not that it has anything to do with you !' she added firmly.

He laughed. ' We both know exactly what it has to do with me !' he retorted. ' It doesn't suit you to be coy, Camilla.'

' Oh, I'm not !' she protested.

He grinned at her. ' And don't look like that either, or I shall give way to the temptation to kiss you—hard !'

' At the breakfast table?' she reproved him, her eyes dancing.

' *That* won't prevent me !'

With his eyes on her mouth, she thought she knew exactly what he was thinking and it brought the colour storming into her cheeks.

' I—I'd object. What would you do then?'

He stood up, towering over her chair and, stooping, kissed her lightly on the cheek. ' *Will you object?*' he pressed her.

She shook her head. ' N-no,' she admitted. ' But this is neither the time nor the place. My mother will be down at any moment !'

He shrugged his shoulders and moved away from her. ' Isn't she breakfasting in bed?'

'I don't think so,' Camilla said briefly.

In this she was quite right, for at that moment her mother came through the door and seated herself opposite her daughter at the table, her curious eyes going from one blank face to the other.

'You must think me a terrible chaperone,' she said meaningly to the Duke, trying not to laugh.

'Not at all,' he returned politely.

'But so early in the morning!' Mrs Armstrong went on. 'I hold you responsible, duke, as Camilla tells me that she is prepared to do anything you tell her to!'

Manoel's mouth tightened angrily. 'If you were not Camilla's mother—' he began.

Mrs Armstrong put her head on one side, laughing up at him. 'I've never pretended to be a particularly good mother,' she cut him off, pausing dramatically when she saw that she had his attention. 'But then I've always had the thought that my husband made an even worse father to sustain me. Have you thought of that?'

'It had crossed my mind to wonder about him,' Manoel admitted. 'Do you know where he is?'

Mrs Armstrong looked put out. 'He farms in Australia, I believe,' she said indifferently.

'You have his address?' Manoel insisted quietly.

'What if I have?'

'Have you got his address?' Camilla asked her, more astonished than she could say.

'Yes, I have,' Mrs Armstrong admitted. She recited it there and then, a touch of bitterness in her voice. 'He won't come back to Europe,' she added.

'But we could have gone with him out there!' Camilla suggested.

Her mother's expression set in the familiar, deliberately charming lines. 'You were too young to have an opinion then, and you know nothing about his life now,' she said mildly. 'I had no intention of burying myself alive

146

in the Outback! We parted company and neither of us have ever regretted it!'

'Does Dennis know where he is?' Camilla asked curiously.

Her mother looked momentarily embarrassed. 'I think I did give him the address once,' she admitted.

'But not to me?'

'Dennis would never go so far as to go to Australia!' her mother explained. 'I wanted to have you children with me!'

'But Camilla might have gone to Australia?' Manoel said sternly.

Mrs Armstrong surveyed her daughter thoughtfully. 'I thought so then. Now she's grown up, I'm not so sure. She has my share of independence and more! I can't see her following any man across the world on his say-so. He didn't even ask *me*, I might say. He just came home one day and waved the tickets in my face!'

Manoel chuckled. 'He had the right to expect you to go with him—'

'You have to say that!' Mrs Armstrong accused him. 'I couldn't see that he had any such right, let me tell you!'

'And have regretted your decision ever since?' he suggested quietly.

Camilla thought that she had never seen her mother so angry. 'I think he might have consulted her,' she said uneasily. 'Why should he go so far as to buy the tickets before he told her?'

Manoel shrugged. 'The man is the head of the household,' he remarked. 'I should expect my wife to abide by my decisions.'

'Wouldn't you even ask her?' Camilla demanded.

'It would depend,' he said thoughtfully. 'I don't think she would have cause for complaint?' He looked her straight in the eyes. 'Would you expect your husband to submit to your will? Or you to his?'

'I'd prefer to discuss things together,' Camilla answered promptly.

'And if you could not agree?'

She licked her lips. 'I'd—I'd give way,' she admitted.

'And not only to her husband!' her mother put in nastily. 'Really, Camilla!'

'I'm sorry, Mother,' Camilla said humorously. 'I think I would have gone to Australia to find my father too. In fact I'm sure I would have done when we first started up in London—'

'*He* wouldn't have helped you!'

Camilla looked suddenly desolate. 'I don't remember him at all!' she cried out. The feel of Manoel's hands on her shoulders comforted her. 'I don't suppose I should really have tried to get to know him,' she added. 'I was so desperate for Camilla Enterprises to be a success that I hadn't time for anything else.'

'You were always more single-minded than Dennis,' her mother said complacently. 'He had time to come to Lisbon and fall in love!'

'Anyone would fall in love with Leonor!' Camilla exclaimed loyally.

Mrs Armstrong preened herself carefully. 'There was no need to keep him so short of money, my dear,' she criticised Camilla in reluctant tones. 'A man needs a bit of cash when he's courting!'

Camilla turned away, hurt. 'He's always had more than I have from the firm,' she said confusedly.

'The firm has been able to afford more for a long time, though, surely? You've been quite generous as far as I've been concerned recently.'

'Yes,' Camilla agreed heavily. She couldn't bear to even look at Manoel. She had never known a more humiliating moment, she thought, and wished that her mother could have at least have spared her his presence when she talked about her finances.

Manoel's fingers bit into her shoulders, bruising her flesh.

Her mother's laughter filled the room. 'Why, Camilla, I believe you're embarrassed that the Duke has discovered that your mother is a remittance woman of sorts! He had to know some time, my dear. I can't exist on thin air.'

'No, Mother.'

Manoel looked severely down at the two of them. 'I fancy that such a subject is not to Camilla's taste. It is something which is better discussed in private. I prefer, at this moment, to think of more pleasant things. To-night, if you are both agreeable, we shall go out and I shall show you some of the things that Lisbon has to offer after dark?'

'Oh, thank you, Manoel!' Camilla exclaimed.

'Are you going to make up a party?' Mrs Armstrong asked eagerly, forgetting everything else at the prospect of going out.

'If you wish me to,' Manoel answered easily.

'I do! I shall need a partner at least! I met several charming people last time I was in Lisbon. There was a man called Rodriguez, I remember, Henri Rodriguez. But then that name is as popular here as Smith is in England, isn't it?'

'I am acquainted with Henri Rodriguez,' Manoel said fastidiously. 'I think he will *not* make a good choice, however—'

Mrs Armstrong smiled charmingly up at him.

'Whatever you say, duke,' she said placidly. 'I'm sure I'll fit in with just about anybody!'

Camilla smiled slowly up at Manoel. 'Wouldn't— wouldn't you rather be on your own?' she asked him shyly.

His smile was warm and affectionate, bringing a lump to her throat. ' Not tonight,' he said.

Camilla dressed carefully for the evening. She wore a long dress, made of a tapestry type material that glowed with two colours of the Tudor era. The only piece of jewellery she had which was suitable was a piece she had designed herself, a primitive shape beaten out of copper intermingled with dull brass. She wore it low, so that it fell into the cavity between her breasts, glinting in any light that was going as she breathed.

But, if she had hoped to outdo her mother, she was doomed to disappointment. Mrs Armstrong had spent the afternoon at a hairdresser she had been to once before on a previous visit to Lisbon, and she had come home with an elaborate hair-do, reminiscent of a goddess from the Olympian heights of ancient Greece. Her dress was of fine scarlet silk, edged with gold matching the slave bracelet on her arm and the long, dangling ear-rings that fell almost to her shoulders.

' Will I do, dear?' she asked her daughter as she came slowly down the stairs.

' Magnificent!' Camilla assured her.

' I like to keep my end up,' her mother sniffed, playing with a chiffon hanky. ' Especially as we don't know what the competition is going to be!'

But Camilla was barely listening, for at that moment Manoel appeared in the hall below her, looking so splendid that her breath was taken away by the sight of him. He was dressed wholly in black, except for his crisp, silver shirt and grey tie, held in place with a pearl pin of such dimensions that she could hardly believe it was real.

He bowed easily over her mother's hand, contenting himself with a brief smile in her direction.

' Are we ready to leave?' he asked them formally.

Even Mrs Armstrong was sufficiently overcome to do

no more than nod her assent. She followed Manoel to the front door and allowed herself to be handed into the car without uttering a single syllable. Camilla got quickly into the back, seating herself immediately behind her mother so that she could see Manoel's profile whenever she looked in his direction. She tried to persuade herself that the thrill of pleasure that it gave her every time she gave way to that particular temptation was only because of the magnificence of his attire, but she knew it was more than that. The strong lines of his face and the way his eyes crinkled at the edges when he smiled were sheer joy to her. She had never thought that any man's looks would mean so much to her, but she was honest enough to admit it frankly to herself. She was falling deeper and deeper in love with Manoel every moment that she stayed in his house.

Manoel drove to the Alcantara district. He explained that the name was another relic of Portugal's Moorish past, coming directly from the Arabic word for a bridge. The streets were very narrow in places, he apologised, so he could not take the car as near to the *fado* house as he would have wished. Mrs Armstrong graciously assured him that she quite understood and she hurried Camilla out of the car and on to the narrow white cobbled pavement by the side of the road.

'We shall wait here,' she said, smoothing down her skirt.

Manoel's luxurious car swept away from them, turning down the first corner to the left. A few minutes later he came walking towards them down the street, his shoes ringing against the cobbles as if they were tipped with metal.

'It is down this way,' he told them, pointing down a small, even narrower street. 'Are you afraid? You have no need to be while I am with you!'

'What would we be afraid of?' Camilla laughingly

asked him.

'Someone might jump out and pull your honey hair!' he answered. 'They might not know that you are English and used to looking after yourself!'

'They'd soon find out!' Camilla said, her face tip-tilted towards him.

'It is not a risk I care to take,' he retorted.

Something in his voice reminded her how easily she had given way to him whenever he had chosen to kiss her. She wondered with a touch of panic if he thought that she would allow any presentable man to kiss her in the same way. To her relief he tucked her hand into his arm and smiled at her.

'It is time someone took care of you,' he added, 'as you won't believe that you have any particular effect on the male sex!'

'Oh, Manoel,' she said weakly.

'And don't look at me like that,' he went on for her ears alone, 'because there is nothing I can do about it now!'

'D-do you want to?' she stammered.

'One day I'll tell you about that!'

His words brought a glow of pleasure to her face and she looked truly beautiful as she followed her mother into the colourful entrance of the *fado* house. The crowing cock, to be seen all over Portugal, covered the wall in an amateurly painted mural, vying with the wrought-iron ornaments that hung from the massive wooden beams and the rough-cast walls. In one corner of the room was a small shrine built around a rather trite statue of Our Lady of Fatima. Camilla noticed that the flowers were real ones, spread out at the feet of the statue. There was also a green stain on the wall, showing where the rain had come in some time in the past.

The room was already crowded with people perched precariously in every available space. A middle-aged

woman in national costume took them to a table close to
the rail that marked off some of the tables that had been
placed on a kind of platform. Her natural cheerfulness
was infectious.

'*Faz favor, sente-se aqui!*'

'*Obrigada*,' Camilla responded.

The woman smiled directly at her, commenting on the
colour of her hair and the noble company she was with.
'I hope you have a pleasant evening,' she added in English, and hurried away, squeezing past the overcrowded
tables, with a word here and there as she went.

Manoel stood for a moment, looking about the room.
'I think my other guests have not arrived yet,' he explained. He smiled and nodded to someone across the
room. Immediately a cry went up round the room.

'Manoel! Manoel! *Faz favor*, Manoel!'

Mrs Armstrong patted the seat beside her. 'Sit down,
dear boy! What do they want you to do? And why do
they all call you Manoel? I shouldn't have thought
you'd have stood for that!'

'Why not?' Manoel said. 'It is my name.'

'Portugal is a republic!' Camilla put in knowledgeably.

Manoel grinned at her. 'It is better than being called
Duke!' he added.

Camilla laughed with him. 'Like a dog!'

'I don't know what you two are talking about!' Mrs
Armstrong complained. 'I feel quite conspicuous at
this table!'

'It is me they want,' Manoel reassured her calmly.
'They want me to sing. Do you mind if I oblige them?'

'Will you sing *fado*?' Camilla asked him, much excited.

His eyes rested on her face and he was smiling. 'I
am told it is not as exciting for a man to sing *fado* as
when a woman does so.'

'Why not?' Camilla demanded.

'We haven't the right timbre to the voice—'

'Please sing, Manoel!' she begged him. 'I've only heard Leonor that once and I've been longing to hear some more.'

'Leonor is a fine *fadista*. You won't find me in the same class!' he warned her.

'I don't care!'

'Camilla is easily pleased,' Mrs Armstrong said, smiling resolutely. 'She has no ear for real music.'

' "*How many times in speaking,*
   *do we not know how to express ourselves.*
   *Hearing a speech is to listen,*
   *hearing a fado is to feel,*" ' he quoted softly. 'That is how it is for us Portuguese. Perhaps you will find that is how it will be for you!'

He bowed politely to Mrs Armstrong, smiling about him as he moved across the room towards the platform at the far end. On the stage, he looked taller than ever, a thin pencil of a figure in black. A couple of men in national costume, made by the simple expedient of sewing some brass buttons on the side of their shabby trousers, and by wearing a long scarlet cummerbund around their waists, appeared from nowhere. Someone else handed them up their guitars and they strummed a note or two by themselves, waiting for Manoel's signal before they began in earnest.

Manoel stood, his whole attitude one of negligent elegance. Then, quite suddenly, he turned his face slightly, opened his mouth and out poured the raucous note of the genuine *fado*, with such ease and volume that Camilla was astonished. The sound of it was exciting to a degree. She could feel it tingling in every nerve of her body, loving her, touching her, in a way she had only previously experienced in Manoel's arms when he had kissed her. The words meant nothing to her. It was the sheer animal fascination of the notes that held her transfixed, totally unable to resist Manoel's attraction for her.

The song had come to an end before she realised that half the people in the restaurant were looking at her and not at Manoel at all. She felt herself blush as they began to applaud and wondered for the first time what Manoel had been singing about. And then she knew, as certainly as if she had understood every word. She remembered the words for hair and honey and knew that he had addressed the whole *fado* to her, the lady whose hair was made of spun honey, stolen from the pathway of the moon as she ran towards the arms of the rising sun. The hair of honey cast a spell on all who came within its radiance, warming their hearts and their lives.

Manoel returned the microphone to its stand came back to their table, exchanging jokes with the other patrons as he pushed his way through the forest of chairs.

' It was a beautiful performance!' Mrs Armstrong told him warmly as he sat down.

Manoel thanked her gravely. ' I am not as good as my brother was,' he said abruptly. ' He always made up his own words—'

' And you do not?' Camilla asked him gently.

To her surprise his smile became embarrassed. ' Sometimes,' he said gruffly.

' I thought it was beautiful!' she exclaimed.

' Then I am amply rewarded,' he answered politely.

There were some other people on the stage now mechanically performing one of the local folk dances. Manoel explained that this was an amateur group who made the rounds of the local *fado* houses, earning a few coins in each which helped them to eke out their living, or to continue their studies, and to give pleasure to other people at the same time.

In the middle of the dance, Camilla saw Dona Victoria and her mother coming towards them. She turned indignantly to Manoel.

'Did you ask *them*?' she asked, her displeasure plain to see.

'No, I did not,' he replied lazily. 'I asked only an old friend of my father's to escort your mother.'

Camilla felt foolish. 'Oh,' she said.

His eyes quizzed her wickedly. 'I thought you liked Dona Joana?' he murmured.

'I do!'

'Then it is Dona Victoria who has succeeded in annoying you?'

Camilla gave him a resentful look. 'No, not at all!' she said airily.

'Liar!'

'I refuse to discuss it!' she said sharply.

'You have no cause to be jealous of Dona Victoria, or *anyone else*!' he said quietly. 'And certainly it would be a mistake to let her see that you are!' He rose with every sign of pleasure and bowed over Dona Joana's hand.

'We have just missed hearing you sing, I am told,' the Portuguese woman greeted him, her eyes twinkling.

'I am sure you won't allow it to ruin your evening!' Manoel retorted dryly.

'Certainly not! If all I hear is true, it more likely saved it!' Dona Joana assured him. 'But we mustn't keep you. We heard it rumoured that there was to be some particularly fine *fado* later on and Senhor Rodriguez kindly agreed to escort us here.'

At the mention of Henri Rodriguez, Camilla could feel the hairs pricking on the back of her neck. She looked up, straight into the eyes of Dona Victoria, and was surprised to see that the Condessa was smiling agreeably at her.

'How soon will you be returning to England?' that lady asked sweetly.

156

Camilla felt baffled. ' I'm not sure,' she said.

Dona Victoria looked amused. ' I thought it would be soon,' she said. ' Now that there is nothing to keep you here in Lisbon.'

' There is Luis—' Camilla began.

The Condessa's eyes became as hard as pebbles. ' Isn't he going home to his mother?'

' When she and Dennis get back—'

' They are back! Didn't you know? How strange! I had made sure that you would be the first to know seeing that he is your brother!'

Camilla also thought it was strange, but she made no comment. ' Have you seen them?' she asked demurely. ' I thought you didn't know Leonor?'

' She is billed to sing here later this evening. Isn't that why you are here?' Her tones were like warm liquid, but Camilla knew her dislike of the Condessa was returned with interest.

Camilla looked demure. ' I am here as Manoel's guest.'

She had the satisfaction of seeing Dona Victoria's expression change to one of anger. ' For the moment!' she snapped.

The Portuguese ladies passed on to their own table. Mrs Armstrong patted her Grecian hair-style into position with a self-conscious air.

' Dona Joana really should not wear black!' she said in clearly audible tones. ' She is one of the few Portuguese women I have seen who looks completely washed out and sad! There is something funereal about all this black!'

Camilla thought privately that it was a great deal more dignified than the women she knew who pretended to be young for ever.

' It depends what you're used to,' she said.

Her mother turned on her. ' *You* can say that? My dear, you'd never sell a *thing* to anyone over thirty in

157

this country.'

Camilla allowed her eyes to wander over the women in the restaurant, noting the number of trouser suits and even a few extremely short skirts.

'The women here are a different shape from most English women,' she observed professionally, 'but their taste doesn't seem so very different.'

She half-turned towards the stage as someone beat a roll on the drum and was just in time to see her sister-in-law stalk through the door, looking neither to the right nor to the left, as she made her way towards the stage. The silence was such that the sound of someone pouring out a glass of wine could be heard all over the restaurant.

Leonor pulled her black shawl up over her head and stood on the edge of the stage, her feet apart and her chin stuck up into the air. She looked as though she hadn't even noticed the pressure of the people about her. Then, with her eyes tight shut and her voice breaking with pain, she sang her heart out, the tears flowing freely down her contorted cheeks.

## CHAPTER XI

'That is about the most awful noise I've ever heard!' Mrs Armstrong said as Leonor drew to an agonised finish.

Manoel's dark eyes were blandly indifferent. 'I expect you will like the other singing and the dancing better.'

'I certainly hope so!'

Camilla sat rigidly upright on her chair, trying to damp down the ardent emotions that the *fado* had aroused within her. To her it was more than singing, or noise, or even music. It was naked interpretation of all feeling in sound. She had heard it called the sadness of Portugal, and it was sad, but richly sad, ennobling the listener as much as the singer.

Leonor swept off the stage without acknowledging the storm of applause. She looked as though she hadn't even heard it, but was still in some other place of her own, where she was alone with the storming emotions of the *fado*.

' Will you ask her to join us?' Camilla asked Manoel.

Mrs Armstrong uttered a feminine little shriek. ' Is that *her*? Is that my new daughter-in-law?'

' Yes, that's Leonor,' Camilla answered her.

' I'm surprised she hasn't given herself a sore throat!' Mrs Armstrong commented with ill-concealed distaste. ' Do you suppose Dennis is here too?'

Manoel stood up. ' I will find out,' he said. ' If you will excuse me?'

Camilla lapsed back into silence, dreamily watching him cross the room.

' I'm not sure I admire your taste, dear,' her mother remarked. ' He may be a duke, but he doesn't like me at all!'

' He invited you,' Camilla reminded her quietly.

' I'd love to know why! I'm not helping him to get better acquainted with you! He must have known that I wouldn't, too, just by being here.'

Camilla sighed. ' I keep telling you, Mother, that the Portuguese understand this kind of arrangement. We don't.'

' My dear child! The Portuguese aren't made differently from anyone else!'

' Perhaps not,' Camilla admitted. ' But they go about it differently!'

' I've never noticed it!' Mrs Armstrong assured her.

' You wouldn't have done! All the same, no one thinks Jaime should have married Leonor. Manoel told me himself that he would have looked after her—and Luis too! It's understood here.'

'So it may be,' her mother said disapprovingly. 'One can see the results for oneself. I suppose Leonor would have been taken in by Manoel as a member of his domestic staff—until she found something she liked better!'

'I don't know,' Camilla admitted.

'Is that what you want?' her mother jeered.

'I don't know what I want!'

Mrs Armstrong patted her **Grecian hair**-do complacently. 'I don't suppose you do. At least you realise that Manoel isn't going to marry you! I think you ought to go straight back to England, now that Leonor is home again, and do some work, my girl!'

'Why?' Camilla asked faintly.

'It's been expensive coming to Lisbon—'

'Then you must allow me to reimburse you,' Manoel's voice said grimly behind them.

Mrs Armstrong, not at all put out, turned her head and welcomed him with a smile. 'I couldn't allow that!'

'Nor can I allow you to make Camilla miserable,' he returned, almost casually. 'She and I understand one another very well.'

'Do you?' Mrs Armstrong drawled. 'I think a mother has some rights when it comes to people taking advantage of her daughter!'

Manoel's stony expression frightened Camilla, but it had no visible effect on her mother.

'No one has taken such effective advantage of your children as you have,' he said menacingly. '*That* is something which will not continue for very much longer. Only the fact that you are a guest under my roof has prevented me from speaking about it before!'

Mrs Armstrong laughed. 'You don't have to spare my feelings!' she told him.

'I doubt if you have any,' he stated with studied insolence. 'It is Camilla's feelings that I am at pains to spare!'

'Manoel!' Camilla protested.

'I apologise,' he said without the faintest sign of any sorrow. 'I find it incredible, however, that any mother would cast her children adrift, to live on their wits, from the tender age of seventeen!'

'Dennis was eighteen, nearly nineteen,' Camilla contradicted him automatically.

Manoel started. 'He is *older* than you?'

Camilla nodded, trying not to smile. 'Fifteen months older.'

'Is it possible? And yet it is you who manage the whole business?'

'My naturally bossy nature!' she said wryly.

'Undoubtedly,' he answered quellingly. 'I don't know why I had imagined that you were the elder.'

Mrs Armstrong watched them crossly. 'I didn't cast them off!' she denied angrily. 'It was their own decision to go.'

Manoel ignored her. 'Leonor is here on her own,' he told Camilla. 'Dennis is coming to collect her at the end of the evening.'

'I want to see my son now!' Mrs Armstrong exclaimed.

'Then Leonor is here alone?' Camilla said eagerly. 'Is she coming to join us?'

Manoel smiled faintly. 'She is,' he confirmed.

They only had to wait a few minutes before Leonor re-entered the restaurant, her head held high, and made her way over to their table.

'Don Felipe has just come in,' she murmured to Manoel. 'He will be coming over in a few minutes.'

'Ah, good.' For the first time since Leonor had finished singing, Manoel glanced towards Mrs Armstrong. 'I invited Dom Felipe to escort you. I think you will find that you have much in common.'

Leonor spluttered with laughter. '*Queria qualquer*

*coisa para beber,'* she said pacifically. She found a packet of cigarettes and went to light one for herself. *'Importa-se que fume?'* she asked Mrs Armstrong.

'I don't understand you,' Mrs Armstrong said, slowly and clearly.

'Do you mind if she smokes?' Camilla translated. She caught Manoel's eyes on her and blushed.

'You are beginning to understand very well,' he congratulated her.

'That wasn't very difficult,' she answered.

'It pleases me to know that you are learning my language,' he smiled at her. 'I expect Leonor will help you now that she has returned to Lisbon?'

Leonor managed to look sulky. 'Why do you want to learn?' she asked.

'We might open a branch of Camilla Enterprises here,' Camilla told her.

'Here? In Lisbon?' Leonor's face burst into animated smiles. 'A very important branch? That will keep Dennis very busy? That will be exactly right!'

Camilla bit her lip, reflecting that about Leonor at least, Manoel had certainly been right.

'Why did you come home so soon?' she asked her. 'Did you miss Luis?'

Leonor shrugged. 'A little. But I am not alive anywhere but in Lisbon! We stayed away the one night only, then we came home to the house in the Alfama. We knew that there was nobody there.' She stopped, her eye suddenly caught by Mrs Armstrong's hair-do. She laid a hand on Camilla's arm, her eyes wide. 'But this must be a relation of yours!' she exclaimed. 'In a way, she is quite like you, no?'

Camilla grinned. 'This is my mother. Mother, may I introduce you to your daughter-in-law, Leonor?'

Mrs Armstrong's eyes were fixed on Leonor's face. 'Where did Dennis meet you?' she demanded.

Leonor smiled at her placidly. 'Dennis heard me sing,' she said simply. 'On the very first night that he came to Lisbon. He had never heard *fado* before and pouff, he fell in love, just like that!'

Mrs Armstrong's eyes glinted as she leaned forward. 'How extraordinary that neither of my children should have any sense of music!'

Camilla waited for the explosion, but she had forgotten the respect in which all Portuguese hold their elders.

'You did not like my singing?' Leonor enquired mildly.

'I thought it a terrible noise!'

Leonor shrugged, laughing a little. 'You have to give yourself to the music,' she told her mother-in-law. 'This is easier, I think, for warm-blooded people. We Portuguese are very warm-blooded!'

'And we are not?' Mrs Armstrong enquired.

Leonor's eyes flashed. 'You are pleasant and have much security,' she opined, 'but warm-blooded? No, I should not say so!'

'But Dennis—' Camilla protested.

'Dennis is a good husband, no more, no less,' Leonor said firmly.

Camilla swallowed any further protest, aware of Manoel's amused eyes watching her.

'Does it bother you not to be warm-blooded?' he asked her.

'Of course not!' she disclaimed with dignity.

He laughed in the back of his throat. 'The ice-maiden who is not an ice-maiden! It is well that only I know about that!'

She blushed, refusing to look at him. 'Are you going to sing again, Leonor?' she asked.

'If you wish me to,' the Portuguese girl agreed. She looked across at Manoel with frankly curious eyes and he nodded slightly, bringing a smile to her lips. 'But you did not tell me!' she exclaimed.

'You weren't here to tell!' he retorted.

Three young men sang 'My Bonnie lies over the ocean' in such soulful tones that some of the tourists began to join in, making the most of what they suspected would be the only song in their own language that evening.

'They always sing this song!' Leonor said impatiently. 'What does it mean? Tell me that! I shall go now and sing again!'

She was as good as her word, crossing the restaurant as soon as the last bars of the Scottish melody twanged from the guitars, imperiously holding up her hand and dismissing the young men on the stage.

Camilla was so busy watching Leonor that she didn't immediately notice the stooped figure of an elderly priest standing patiently beside their table until he tapped her lightly on the shoulder with a long, bony finger. She started, twisting round in her chair to face him. He put up a finger to his lips and slipped silently into the seat beside her.

'The *fadista* is about to sing!' he whispered.

She remembered that it was considered bad manners to talk when a *fado* was being sung, no matter how indifferent the singer, and turned her attention back to Leonor, hunched beneath her black fisherwoman's shawl, preparing to sing.

When the pure sound rang through the room, it was still a shock to the waiting audience. Leonor's voice rose and fell, perfectly controlled, but always on the edge of a scream.

'*Que saudade!*' Dom Felipe whispered as the last notes died away.

Mrs Armstrong shivered. 'She might have been singing inside my spine!' she muttered.

'But no, *senhora*,' the priest rebuked her. 'This

164

feeling, this "*saudade*" is the quintessence of the Portuguese. It is the ultimate sadness mixed with the ultimate joy! One is on the edge of tears and laughter both! Your daughter understands what this means because she abandons her heart to the music.'

'I deny that it is music!' Mrs Armstrong replied firmly.

The priest only smiled. 'It is the music of love,' he told her. 'But first you must know love.'

Mrs Armstrong pursed her lips. She looked suddenly old and sad. Camilla felt suddenly sorry for her and, wondering a little at herself, she put her hand affectionately on hers, calling her attention to the menu.

'What are you going to eat, Mother?' she asked her.

Mrs Armstrong perused the card briefly. 'I don't understand a word of it!' she wailed. 'No doubt the Duke will choose for all of us, no matter what we want!' she added caustically.

Dom Felipe smiled nervously. 'I prefer to choose for myself,' he said, clearing his throat. 'It is a man's privilege!'

He and Manoel had a long discussion about the relative qualities of the various dishes, both of them ignoring the women as they made their decision. Camilla considered asking if she could try the fresh sardines that are so popular in Portugal, but Manoel made no move to consult her, ordering for them all in brief, businesslike tones that brooked no argument.

There was a moment's silence when he had finished. Dom Felipe sipped his wine thoughtfully and then, as if he had quite made up his mind that the silence had gone on too long, he turned to Mrs Armstrong, waiting until he had her complete attention.

'It is beautiful to me to be back in Portugal again,' he began. 'Manoel will have told you that I am recently returned from Australia? Not, alas, Queensland, where your husband is. I was in New South Wales.'

'Really?' Mrs Armstrong interjected with supreme lack of interest.

'How long is it before you go there yourself?' the priest went on.

Mrs Armstrong's mouth opened. 'I?' she asked blankly.

Dom Felipe looked embarrassed. He swivelled in his chair, seeking for support from Manoel, but the Duke merely slouched lower in his chair, his eyes lazy and amused.

'But I understood you were joining your husband quite shortly!' the poor man explained.

'Never!' Mrs Armstrong retorted flatly.

Camilla gave Manoel an astonished glance. 'Did you remember my father's address?' she accused him.

'I wrote to him, yes,' he admitted calmly.

'How dare you?' Mrs Armstrong demanded.

But Manoel only went on smiling. 'I told him you were still alone and that now that both your children are settled, you will have need of his care for you,' he said, just as though it were the most natural thing in the world. 'I have told him it would be best for him to come to Lisbon and for you to return to Australia with him. He will wish to see for himself that Camilla's future is secure, and he will probably like to see Dennis and Leonor also.'

Camilla stared at him blankly across the table. The look in his eyes made her want to throw herself into his arms and to tell him that she loved him.

'She won't go!' she said baldly.

'Who says I won't go?' her mother cut across furiously. 'I shall do as I like!'

'Just as you always have?' Dom Felipe suggested dryly.

She gave him a brilliant smile. 'Yes,' she said, her head held high. 'Just as I always have!'

Dennis was not at all surprised to find that his mother was staying under the Ferrado roof. He kissed her on the cheek and sat down beside her, complimenting her lightly on the audacity of her hair-style.

'So you've met Leonor?' he said with a smile.

'Oh, Dennis!' Mrs Armstrong exclaimed. 'Why didn't you tell me? You must have known when I saw you in Lisbon before! I'm hurt!'

'Are you, dear?'

'You knew I would be!' she complained. 'I wouldn't have interfered!'

'Oh yes, you would,' he contradicted her. 'You'd have been in it up to your pretty neck! It was bad enough having Camilla wanting to dress the bride, and not wanting to come to Lisbon anyway because she'd heard you were here, without having you on our backs too!'

He looked across the table and grinned at Camilla.

'I didn't know you had seen Mother when you came here on holiday,' she said in a small voice.

Dennis looked ashamed. 'I meet her now and again. I always meant to tell you, Camilla, but you don't invite that kind of confidence.'

'I suppose not,' she admitted.

'Children!' Mrs Armstrong protested. 'I refuse to be discussed as if I were some kind of a bad odour. Dennis doesn't have to ask your permission for *everything* he does, Camilla!'

Camilla was hurt. Had she really tried to run Dennis's whole life for him? Unexpectedly, it was Manoel who came to her defence. 'A man only asks a woman's permission if he wants to,' he said flatly.

'Not in Camilla Enterprises!' Dennis retorted, laughing.

'I should not see the need in any circumstances!' Manoel replied implacably. 'But then I can't imagine myself working for a woman in the first place!'

' *Touché!* ' Dennis grinned.

' But Dennis doesn't work *for* me,' Camilla said automatically. ' We work *together*!'

' Rubbish!' said Dennis.

Camilla flared up angrily. ' It is not rubbish!' she denied vigorously.

' Isn't it? Since when did I have any say in a major policy decision?'

Camilla stared at him. ' Always!' she said weakly.

' When?' he insisted.

Camilla reviewed all that had happened in the firm for the last year. She was dismayed to discover that she couldn't honestly think of a single suggestion of Dennis's that had been finally adopted.

' You have your way over all sale techniques,' she insisted.

' Big deal!'

' But you were wrong about people not wanting—' She broke off, seeing his quizzical expression. ' I suppose that's not the point?' she admitted.

' Not exactly, honey.'

Manoel's eyes glinted with sudden interest. ' Honey,' he repeated. ' It is an endearment that suits you, my dear.'

Camilla gave him an impatient glance. ' But I'm not as bossy as he'd have you believe!' she cried out. ' I'll prove it to you! When can I see you properly, Dennis? There's a policy decision that needs to be made right now—'

' Oh?' he quizzed her.

' About opening a branch in Lisbon!'

' Are we going to?'

' Yes, we are!'

' Then there doesn't seem to be much to talk about,' he pointed out reasonably.

Camilla saw far too late the trap she had fallen into. She wouldn't have minded, she thought, if it hadn't been for the indecent delight in her mother's eyes at her discomfiture. She had not known that her mother disliked her so much, or that it had had anything to do with Dennis.

'There's a great deal to talk about!' she answered gamely. 'I'm thinking of selling Camilla Enterprises.'

'You going to do *what*?' Dennis demanded.

Camilla swallowed nervously. 'We can't discuss it here,' she said warningly, glancing at the tired face of Dom Felipe. 'I was waiting until you got back from your honeymoon.'

'Right,' said Dennis. 'I'll be round to see you first thing in the morning. I'll take Luis back to his mother at the same time.'

'All right,' she agreed stiffly.

Dennis forced a smile, turning to Manoel. 'Will you be there?' he asked.

Camilla said, 'No,' in explosive tones, but Manoel silenced her with a gesture.

'Why do you ask?' he asked Dennis quietly.

Dennis shrugged. 'I didn't think a Ferrado could resist the temptation of interfering in my affairs—'

'That's not fair!' Camilla almost shouted at him.

Her brother gaped at her. 'My, my,' he said. 'You'll be saying next that you want his support to see you through the interview with me!'

'That scarcely goes with my bossy image!'

'Perhaps you're afraid that the worm might turn?'

'Why should I be?' she demanded.

'I had something to do with building up Camilla Enterprises. If you sell, what are you going to live on?'

Camilla blenched. 'I hadn't thought,' she admitted.

'You don't intend to sell at all!' Dennis jeered at her. 'Nothing's too good for you to use as a pawn in the game you're playing, is it?'

Camilla gave him a long, level look. 'Shall we wait until tomorrow?' she suggested.

His anger fell away from him as easily as it always did. 'I'm sorry, love. I've had my own troubles recently!'

'You would marry her!' their mother put in. 'I could have told you it wouldn't work!'

Dennis laughed immoderately. 'My poor dear, you're out there! Leonor is far too good for me, as you'll find out if you stay around for long enough.'

Dom Felipe leaned forward, pursing his lips eagerly. 'But then you have not heard, my son—your mother is returning to her husband in Australia!'

Dennis chuckled appreciatively. 'Amen to that!' he exclaimed irreverently.


Manoel's easy way of organising other people constantly surprised Camilla. She would never have thought that her mother would have agreed, and agreed amiably, to being taken home by Dennis and Leonor. But far from making a fuss, her only concern seemed to be that they should also take Dom Felipe with them as they were going directly past his monastery. Manoel himself merely stood beside them, his interest hardly engaged by the proceedings as they wished one another goodnight and packed into the two waiting cars.

'Very neat!' Camilla commented as Manoel handed her into his own car.

He grinned at her. 'Did you want them to come with us?' he countered.

She shook her head. 'You know I didn't,' she said.

'I wasn't quite sure,' he told her.

'You had every reason to be,' she said sleepily. 'It seems to me that my feelings are an open book to you!'

He laughed. 'Then selling Camilla Enterprises wasn't entirely bravado?' he teased her.

'I don't know,' she admitted. 'You see,' she added, 'I don't know where I am with you, or even with Dennis any longer. I didn't think his marriage would make such a difference.' She was silent for a long moment. 'I thought we had a partnership,' she tried to explain diffidently, 'but now I'm not so sure.'

'Most partnerships have a dominant element in them,' he remarked.

She looked at him seriously. 'But supposing both elements wanted to do the dominating?'

'One of them would have to give way.'

'And in Camilla Enterprises, it was Dennis?'

'Don't worry about it,' Manoel said gently. 'The talent and the inspiration were yours. It could be that he had less to offer. Don't let him hurt you too, Camilla.'

'He doesn't hurt me,' she said painfully. 'You have to be vulnerable before you can be hurt. I've always seen to it before that I wasn't vulnerable to anyone. I wish I'd never come to Portugal!'

'Because you're vulnerable now?'

She thought of denying it, but she couldn't. The tears started into her eyes. 'You know I am,' she said.

He put a hand over hers, crushing her fingers in his. She felt the familiar thrill of excitement that gripped her whenever Manoel touched her.

'You were right about one thing,' he said in a strained voice. 'It was a mistake to bring your mother to Lisbon. I haven't been alone with you since she got here!'

Camilla gave him a tearful smile. 'Is that why you're making her go to Australia?'

'Partly,' he admitted. 'Mostly it's because if she had wanted to she would have seen nothing against getting a divorce from your father and marrying again. Why did she not do this? I think it must be because she loves him in her own way. It remains to be seen whether he has any feeling for her.'

Camilla's astonishment was easy to see. 'I didn't think you'd agree with divorce,' she said.

'I don't. Any woman who marries me stays married to me for life. You'd better understand that, Camilla!'

'Why should I understand it particularly?' she retorted.

With deliberation he drove the car towards the river, parking it near to the monument to the Discoverers.

'This is why,' he said briefly, without any gentleness. He reached out for her, pulling her into his arms. His lips came down on hers, forcing hers apart, while his hands explored the curves of her body. For an instant she tried to resist him, but her need was as great as his, and she kissed him back, revelling in her own weakness.

'But it isn't enough!' she whispered when she could.

'What isn't enough?'

'*This!*'

'You talk too much,' he sighed. 'Don't you understand yet that I want you as I've never wanted any other woman? And that I mean to have you—'

'Oh yes, I understand *that*!' She drew back from his arms, the tears coursing down her cheeks. 'I thought it was enough, but it isn't!'

He heaved a resigned sigh. 'I thought we'd get back to Camilla Enterprises!' he said.

'And my mother,' she added. 'I thought I could. Manoel, I'm so *sorry*!'

'Then why?'

'She made me feel cheap,' she explained.

She felt him stiffen against her and then she knew that he was laughing. 'Manoel!' she protested.

'I'm sorry, my sweet,' he said apologetically. He pulled her close and kissed her ruthlessly, ignoring her attempts to escape him. '*Now* say that you feel cheap!' he challenged her.

She blushed, knowing well that he had only to touch her to light a fire within her that was hard to damp down, even when she was alone.

'What about Dona Victoria?' she burst out.

'I've told you before that she need not concern you!' he said.

Camilla bit her lip, hiding her face against his shoulder.

'But she does concern me,' she pleaded. 'When she marries you—'

Manoel's fingers bit into her shoulders and he shook her until her hair came loose, a honey-coloured cloud that fell to her shoulders.

'Please, Manoel,' she gasped. 'I know the Portuguese don't speak about these things, but I have to!'

'On the contrary!' he informed her in icy tones. 'We are quite explicit when we decide to marry, and when we decide to take a mistress—'

'Manoel!' she begged. 'Please don't be angry!'

'Angry?' he snorted. 'I could beat you! And I very well may before I've done! Come here and let me kiss you in peace!'

She made a little gesture of submission and her arms went up round the back of his neck. 'Darling,' she said. 'I love you!'

'So I should hope!' he retorted.


## CHAPTER XII

The house was in darkness when Manoel opened the heavy front door and switched on the lights of the magnificent chandeliers in the hall.

'It must be very late,' Camilla whispered guiltily.

'I imagine everyone else is in bed and asleep,' Manoel agreed in amused tones.

Camilla made a face at him. 'I only hope my mother

173

is!'

He frowned at her. 'Do you think that she can touch you now?' he demanded.

She shook her head. 'Nothing can touch me now that I know I have your love,' she smiled at him.

He reached out for her. 'Mistress of all I have,' he said, laughing at her.

She winced, but she responded eagerly to his kiss.

'Manoel,' she said at last, 'you will be there tomorrow when Dennis comes, won't you?'

'If you want me to be.'

She looked up at him, her eyes shy. 'I don't know what to do about Camilla Enterprises,' she admitted.

'I don't know that I can help you there, sweetheart,' he answered. 'Dennis has a right to be consulted. Why don't you wait and see what he says?'

'I will,' she agreed. 'But—'

He smiled encouragingly. 'But what?'

'I want to do what *you* want!'

'My love, if you say things like that I shall keep you down here all night!' He kissed her again softly on the mouth. 'But Camilla Enterprises is your business and you must make your own decision about it.'

'But I can't!' she protested.

'I think you can,' he said. 'It is less unusual now in Portugal for a woman to work, but not many of the richer ones do so. They lead gentle lives, meeting their friends for coffee and afternoon tea, and making a pleasant atmosphere for their husband and children. But you have led a very different life. If you had no work to do, at least at first you might be bored—'

She put her hand over his mouth. 'I can't imagine being bored with you!' she exclaimed.

He chuckled. 'That's now, when you're in a biddable mood—'

'I've never wanted any other man,' she admitted.

' I didn't know, you see—'

' That, my love, is only too obvious!'

' Oh! You shouldn't tease me!' she told him. ' It hurt when you called me an ice-maiden!'

' Did it?' He sounded amused.

' I'd never felt inadequate before,' she confessed. ' I don't know now that I can be all that you want, but I'll try, Manoel. Only be patient with me. It isn't easy to believe that a duke loves me. You have so much history behind you and I—I have only my mother!'

He laughed. ' Without wishing to be rude, I find one of your mother quite enough!' he teased her.

' You know what I meant!' she said crossly. ' I can't help being inexperienced and inadequate. I don't know what you'll expect of me?'

His dark eyes grew warm, making her blush. ' That's easily answered!' he said dryly. ' My ridiculous love, what do you suppose I shall expect of you?'

' I don't know!' she whispered.

He looked at her soberly. ' I only want your love,' he said.

It was her turn to laugh. ' Oh, Manoel, how little you know yourself!' she protested. ' Only my love! Even if I didn't want to, you know you'd make me do exactly what you wanted! And, at the end of it all, you will still be the Duke of Ferrado, but what shall I be?'

' My very dearest love!' he said.


Camilla overslept the next morning. She felt heavy-eyed and her shin hurt where she had barked it trying to get into bed without disturbing the sleeping maid at the foot of her bed. She glanced down at the familiar mound beneath the blankets on the truckle bed, only to find that the girl had already departed. For a moment she considered the luxury of drifting back into sleep, but the thought of Dennis's impending visit drove her from her bed.

At least she would have a bath, she decided, and sauntered into the bathroom to run the water. It came gushing out of the taps, hot and steamy, and she began to feel better at the sight of it.

'*Minha senhorita!*'

Camilla put her head round the door to find that the maid had come back into the room, carrying her breakfast on a tray.

'*O Duque* says you are tired this morning,' she announced with a little giggle. 'It is better that you have your breakfast in your room and not under the eyes of the *senhora* your mother!'

'Is she already up?' Camilla asked, surprised.

The maid shook her head. 'The *senhora* is tired also,' she said. She eyed Camilla speculatively. 'It is a great excitement for us all, *minha senhorita*! Even Senhora Carlota is pleased, though she says we must wait for *o Duque* to announce it himself before we offer you our congratulations! I thought, though, that perhaps you would not mind my saying I am happy for you now, as I have been sleeping in your own room, no?'

'No,' Camilla agreed in complete confusion.

'It is a very happy day for you! You will not object if I tell you that at first we could not believe that such a thing could happen? But all the servants are *very* pleased! We shall all serve you with the same pleasure with which we have always served *o Duque*,' she added virtuously.

'Thank you,' said Camilla. 'Thank you very much.'

The maid nodded happily. She set the tray down on a small table, drawing it up in front of Camilla and urging her to eat and to drink the coffee while it was still hot. She herself went into the bathroom, adding bath salts to Camilla's bath with a lavish hand.

'Shall I be your personal maid?' she asked determinedly as she re-entered the bedroom.

'I've never had a maid,' Camilla said honestly.

The girl was plainly shocked. 'But, *minha senhorita*, who has kept your clothes so beautifully? Who has dressed your hair?'

Camilla stopped a laugh. 'Who has dressed my hair since I have been here?'

The maid gave her a crestfallen look. 'Before, yes,' she recovered herself, but it would not be suitable now! 'The Dona Victoria has *two* maids of her own!' she added persuasively.

Camilla grinned. 'That settles it!' she agreed.

The maid laughed gaily. 'It must be so!' she giggled. 'To be the Duchess of Ferrado is better than to be a countess!'

Camilla's mouth felt suddenly dry. She stared at the girl as though she were looking at a ghost. '*Duchess of Ferrado!*' she echoed. 'But I'm not—'

The girl sighed romantically. 'Naturally you have not thought about it yet,' she said gently.

'I mean that I'm not going to *marry* Manoel!' Camilla insisted.

But the maid only laughed. 'Of course you will marry him! How fortunate you are! Such a man! Do you think you will refuse him?'

Camilla made a last effort to pull herself together before abandoning herself to the wonderful contentment that threatened to engulf her.

'But I can't be the Duchess of Ferrado!' she said faintly.

The maid giggled. 'As soon as you are married to *o Duque*, you will be the Duchess, no?'

Camilla had her bath in a dream. She knew that the maid had jumped to a wrong conclusion, but it was such a lovely thought that she couldn't resist toying with it, turning it over in her mind and wishing that it were true. Manoel had said he would be quite explicit when he wanted a wife or a mistress, and he certainly hadn't asked her to be his wife! But if he did—!

By the time she had dressed, she felt so nervous that it took an act of will to make herself go downstairs. It was a relief to her to find the hall empty and she hesitated at the foot of the steps, trying to decide which room Manoel would prefer her to receive Dennis in. Then the door of the dining room opened and Manoel came into the hall, his face alight with pleasure at the sight of her.

' Good morning,' he said.

She was totally tongue-tied. This was the Duke of Ferrado as well as being the Manoel she loved!

' Did you sleep well?' he asked her, smiling.

' Yes, thank you.'

' So demure?' he teased her. ' Don't you wish me to kiss you this morning?'

She blushed. ' I have to be ready for when Dennis comes,' she said.

' And that prevents you from kissing me?' He looked so hurt that her heart melted within her and she kissed him hurriedly on his cheek. ' I suppose that will have to do,' he said regretfully, eyeing her in a way that unsettled her badly. ' Dennis is already here.'

' Oh,' she said.

' He is in the sitting room,' Manoel went on easily. ' Do you wish me to come with you?'

' Oh *yes*!' She bit her lip. ' I still don't know what to do!' she complained.

' Why don't you let Dennis decide for you?' he suggested.

She gave him a goaded look, surprised to find that her hand had somehow become entwined with his. ' Dennis doesn't like decisions,' she said abruptly. She looked up at him through her eyelashes. ' It isn't that I always want my own way,' she added apologetically. ' You'll
178

see for yourself!'

He laughed. 'Will I?'

She nodded vigorously. 'I'm quite prepared to do whatever you say,' she reminded him shortly.

'But Dennis is involved in a way that I am not,' he answered quietly. 'Why try to decide anything before you have talked to him?'

Dennis was sitting in one of the easy chairs when they went into the sitting room. He had a pile of loose papers in a file on his knee and he looked tired and rather sulky.

'I thought you might bring Leonor with you!' Camilla exclaimed, disappointed.

'She was still asleep when I left,' he answered crossly.

Camilla forced a smile. 'I expect I was too! I'm ashamed to say that I've only just got up.'

Dennis gave her a lopsided smile. 'Acclimatising yourself to a future life of luxury?' he asked her.

She shook her head, a little embarrassed. 'Are—are you enjoying being married?' she began suddenly, in a pathetic attempt to change the subject.

'I'm happy enough!' he responded briefly.

'Is that all?' she pressed him.

'Isn't it enough? Leonor is as strong-minded as you are in her own way. That is one of the reasons why I didn't bring her this morning. She wanted to come back to Lisbon, and I came. She wants to sing *fado* every night, and I've agreed to that. But Camilla Enterprises has nothing to do with her. I'm going to make my own decisions about that!'

'Very well,' she said agreeably.

Manoel smiled wryly at them both. 'I gather that I am *de trop* after all?'

'No, Manoel. You promised you'd stay!'

Manoel looked enquiringly at Dennis. 'Well?'

'Stay, by all means,' Dennis agreed reluctantly. 'It won't make any difference either way. I've already made up my mind what we ought to do.'

'Have you?' Camilla said with respect.

'We'll need a branch here in Lisbon for a start,' Dennis went on. 'Leonor won't live anywhere else. She says she will, but she was visibly wilting after two days away from her beloved Lisbon. I thought I could set it up and manage it. That will leave you free to carry on in London. I never did much there anyway, so you won't miss me all that much!'

'But,' Camilla said very gently, 'I told you, I'm thinking of selling Camilla Enterprises.'

'You can't!' her brother told her robustly. 'I'm not saying it isn't yours to do as you like with, but you have a good thing going there! Why start again with something else that might not pay so well?'

Camilla inspected her hands with interest. 'I'm not sure I want to be a designer and a business woman all my life,' she remarked.

'Oh, come off it, Camilla! Since when have you shown a spark of interest in anything else?'

Camilla only blushed. Dennis watched her, his genuine amazement making her blush still more.

'But, Camilla, you've *always* wanted to be independent of everybody!' he protested.

'I hadn't met Manoel then,' she explained.

Dennis ran a harassed hand through his hair. 'But you know how the Ferrados treated Leonor! How could you, Camilla? I thought you only stayed to guard my interests with Luis? What have you been doing?'

Camilla cast a desperate look at Manoel. 'It's true the old Duke didn't do much for Leonor,' she answered in a small voice, 'but I don't think Manoel is to blame for that! And let me tell you that Jaime didn't have to marry Leonor at all! It's quite understood in Portugal, when there is a disparity between the man's position and —and the woman's, that they should *not* get married.

Nobody thinks anything of it!'

Dennis stared at her open-mouthed. ' You sound like an authority on the subject!' he jeered.

' I am!' Camilla insisted.

' It sounds downright immoral to me!' he said fiercely. ' What about the children?'

' The children have their father's full protection always,' Manoel put in. ' My father expected Jaime to make such an arrangement with Leonor, but my brother refused to do so—as I should have done in his position. I prefer to have the woman I love at my side throughout life and not only in the privacy of my bed at night!'

Camilla felt suddenly weak at the knees. ' But I thought—'

' Good grief, Camilla, are you going to *marry* him?' Dennis gasped.

' I don't know,' she said foolishly.

' You *don't know*?'

' I thought—' She looked helplessly at Manoel. ' Oh, Manoel, are you sure?'

' Quite sure, my simple-minded love,' he said lovingly. ' I am only waiting for your father to arrive to marry you with as much speed as I can. It will be the major social event of the Lisbon season, but we shall have to put up with that, and your mother may even enjoy it!'

Camilla was speechless. Dennis gave her a look of complete disapproval.

' I don't believe that you'd thought of marrying him at all!' he observed in disgust. ' Had you?'

' I—I thought—' Camilla began, unable to wrench her eyes away from the look in Manoel's eyes. ' I'd be proud to share your bed on any terms,' she said finally.

' *Camilla!* ' Dennis roared at her.

' *Anyone* would be!' she went on defiantly. ' And I wouldn't wear black, or grey alpaca, either! It would be—cloth of gold or nothing!'

' Preferably nothing!' Manoel put in, much enjoying himself.

Discomfited, Camilla subsided into complete embarrassment. ' I—I didn't mean that I don't understand why Leonor wore black,' she went on, making bad worse. ' But I'm neither Portuguese nor a widow!'

' I won't have you saying anything against Leonor!' Dennis thundered.

' I think you can be grateful,' Manoel grinned. ' Black is much more respectable than nothing, don't you think?'

' You keep out of this,' Dennis turned on him. ' This is between my sister and myself!'

' On the contrary,' Manoel retorted smoothly, ' I consider that what Camilla wears for our wedding to be my affair rather than yours!'

Outraged, Dennis uttered a strangled gasp. ' You've both gone mad!'

' Yes,' Camilla agreed weakly, ' I think we have! I've forgotten for the moment about Dona Victoria. She— she's much more suitable as a wife.'

' Who is she?' Dennis demanded.

Manoel ignored him. ' I have never been able to share your admiration for Victoria,' he told Camilla solemnly. ' My name is an old and honourable one and *very important* to me. That is why the mother of my children must be proud to bear my name and not be seeking other rewards elsewhere.'

' Don't you *want* to marry a countess?' Camilla demanded.

' I might, if you were a countess—'

' But Dona Victoria—'

' Has other interests!' he said wryly.

Camilla swallowed. ' I didn't think you knew!' she said faintly.

' No,' he agreed without rancour, ' so I gathered. My dear, I may be a duke, but that doesn't mean I'm a fool.

Senhor Rodriguez has a certain reputation of which I have been aware for a long time, long before you came to Lisbon! Though I have some reason to be grateful to him. Not only has he ambitions as far as Victoria is concerned, but when you turned to me after he had accosted you at Luis's *quinta*, I knew for the first time that you were in love with me.'

'Did you?' she said, fascinated. 'I'm surprised you didn't know straight away!'

He laughed gently. 'Attraction, yes, but love? It was too early for me to be sure of that!'

'*Camilla*, will you pay attention to me?' Dennis broke in angrily.

'Yes, of course,' she agreed.

'I can't think what's come over you!' he told her bitterly. 'You're not even *listening*, are you?'

She turned reluctantly away from Manoel, her eyes soft and dazed with sheer happiness. 'Do as you like,' she said. 'But you'll have to find a new designer. I won't go on working after I'm married.'

'But you can design anywhere!' Dennis insisted doggedly.

'I won't have time,' Camilla answered mildly.

'What will you be doing?' Dennis demanded.

Camilla made a comprehensive gesture with her hands. 'There will be the children and so on,' she said.

'So on?' he repeated.

'I fancy that I am included under that heading,' Manoel told him, his eyes dancing.

'I daresay,' Dennis said flatly. 'But what am I supposed to do without Camilla?'

Camilla knotted her fingers together, a little ashamed of Dennis's attitude. 'I want to sell Camilla Enterprises,' she reiterated.

'But why?' her brother demanded.

'I need the money,' she said stubbornly.

'Don't be a fool!' He hesitated, curious despite himself. 'What for?' he asked.

Camilla licked her lips. 'For—a dowry,' she said bravely.

Both men stared at her and the rich colour rolled up her cheeks. 'There is no need for you to bring me a dowry,' Manoel said. 'Darling, don't you know even now that it's *you* I want?'

'But I want to give you something too!' she pleaded with him.

'And what about me?' Dennis asked her again.

She made an impatient movement with one hand. 'I know it won't mean much to you,' she went on to Manoel, 'but I want to bring everything I have to our marriage, then I can accept all that you're giving me. Manoel, please allow me to be a little generous too!'

He looked white and strained and she thought he was going to refuse her, but when he spoke she knew it was only because his feelings were as deeply stirred as hers.

'I have a suggestion to make,' he said. 'I think it would solve every difficulty for us all. Camilla, will you sell Camilla Enterprises to me, with all its assets and goodwill?'

'But you don't want—' she began to protest.

'Can't you Ferrados keep out of *anything*?' Dennis demanded.

'I would merely hold a financial interest,' Manoel went on. 'I know nothing of the fashion and design worlds.'

'Then what good would it do?' Dennis insisted.

'We would have the capital to open a branch in Lisbon, in which you, Dennis, would have a completely free hand in running. We would have to put in a manager in the London office, but that should not be too difficult. And it would mean that Camilla could retain an interest, as I hope she will interest herself in all my business ventures. Isn't that reason enough?'

'I don't see what you'd get out of it, darling,' Camilla objected. 'You would be paying my dowry yourself!'

'No, I should not. We shall arrange for a proper audit of Camilla Enterprises and I shall pay you a fair price for my interest in it. What you do with that price will be your affair—'

'Oh, Manoel, I want you to have it!'

He smiled. 'Then I shall invest it in improving the Ferrado estate. There is much to be done before my son inherits, believe me!'

'Don't I have any say at all in all this?' Dennis asked.

'No,' Camilla teased him. 'We shall do exactly what Manoel tells us to!'

To her surprise he laughed. 'Suits me,' he said lazily. 'I'll be able to make you do some designing for the Lisbon branch, seeing that you'll be so handy!'

'Yes, you will,' Camilla agreed in well satisfied tones, and wondered why both the men burst out laughing.

Luis was the least surprised member of the family that Camilla was to marry Manoel.

'I knew she liked him,' he told Dennis with a lordly air. 'She said she had to work, so she didn't have time to marry Tio, but women only work if they want to, don't they? I knew Tio Manoel would marry her just the same. He kissed her, you see!'

'Yes, and I wish to kiss her again,' Manoel told him sternly, 'so hurry up with your goodbyes and take your stepfather away with you!'

Luis grinned, '*Sim*, Tio!'

He bowed over Camilla's hand in the grand manner, his eyes, which were so like Manoel's, laughing up at her. 'That is the right way with a duchess!'

Camilla laughed. 'Another Portuguese custom?' she asked drolly.

Manoel smiled. 'It is pleasant to show a married

woman respect, don't you think?'

She blushed at the look in his eyes. 'I'm not married yet!' she reminded him.

'But, Camilla, you must hurry!' Luis told her earnestly. 'If I am to come and stay with you, it will be better—'

'Much better!' his uncle cut him off, propelling him forcibly out of the door. 'Dennis, remember me to Leonor and tell her we shall be very happy to see all three of you *some other time*!'

'I will,' Dennis agreed amiably. He took Luis's hand and went out of the front door into the Lisbon sunshine. 'Your grace!' he added with a schoolboy grin, and was gone.

Camilla looked up at Manoel, her eyes wide. 'I hope no one ever calls *me* that!' she exclaimed.

Manoel sighed. 'I always knew that you held my being a duke against me,' he said mildly.

'Especially when you trampled over all my most deeply held principles,' she agreed complacently.

'I think they were not so very deeply held, my love,' he said. 'To be deeply held, principles must be tested, and it is quite clear that you have none at all!'

'Manoel!' she protested.

'How can you have?' he asked reasonably, his voice trembling with laughter, 'I find it quite unprincipled to settle for anything else but marriage!'

'But, Manoel! It was you who told me that the Portuguese understand these arrangements—'

'I do not claim to have all these principles of yours!' he retorted.

'No,' she said bitterly. 'I never thought you had! And you can laugh if you like, but it was *agony* when I thought you would eventually marry someone else! It may be my English blood, but I can't understand—'

His arms went about her in the most satisfactory way.

'Then why would you have agreed to such an arrangement?' he asked teasingly.

She hid her face against him. 'Because,' she said bravely, 'where you are concerned I have no pride, nothing but my love for you!'

He forced up her chin and he was no longer laughing. 'I would not have done that to you,' he said deliberately. 'I thought you understood what I was about. At first, I thought you would be no more than an idle distraction. You were beautiful and your coolness challenged me. Then, when I kissed you, I found you were not so cool as you would have the world believe. But, it seemed to me, you had no one of your own to protect you. I asked your mother to visit my house, thinking that she would support you and give you the courage you needed to think about accepting my proposal to be my wife. But almost her first words to me were that you were willing to be my mistress, but that with your commitments to your family—do you support them all financially, my little darling?—you could not give up your work in Camilla Enterprises.'

Camilla blushed. 'My mother—' she began in a shamed voice.

'Australia will be far enough away for her to be,' Manoel interrupted her masterfully. 'She will be happier with your father and we shall have no further need to worry about her.'

'Yes, Manoel,' Camilla said demurely.

'But yesterday, I was sure that at last you understood,' he went on fiercely. 'I thought you understood that Victoria had no standing with me, that she was of no concern to either of us, and that you had my whole heart?'

'I thought you loved me,' Camilla admitted.

'But not enough to be the mother of my heirs?' he asserted bitterly.

'I—I didn't think—'

He cut her off with a kiss. 'My love, how true!' he observed. 'You didn't think at all!'

But she denied this. 'I thought too much!' She reflected that this was not quite true. 'When I could!' she added judiciously. 'Mostly I just knew I couldn't do without you!'

He began to kiss her again, slowly and expertly, and she abandoned herself to his caresses and to the loving warmth of his nearness where no thought was possible. In Portugal, she had found her love, and the echoes of the *fado*, the song of Portugal, beat an accompaniment to the depths of her love.

# Golden Harlequin Library

## A Treasury of Harlequin Romances!

Many of the all time favorite Harlequin Romance Novels have not been available, until now, since the original printing. But on this special introductory offer, they are yours in an exquisitely bound, rich gold hardcover with royal blue imprint. Three complete unabridged novels in each volume. And the cost is so very low you'll be amazed!

**Handsome, Hardcover Library Editions at Paperback Prices! ONLY $1.95 each volume.**

This very special collection of classic Harlequin Romances would be a distinctive addition to your library. And imagine what a delightful gift they'd make for any Harlequin reader!

Start your collection now. See reverse of this page for **SPECIAL INTRODUCTORY OFFER!**

v

# GOLDEN HARLEQUIN LIBRARY

$1.95 ea. vol.

## EACH VOLUME CONTAINS 3 COMPLETE HARLEQUIN ROMANCES

**Special Introductory Offer**
(First 6 volumes only $9.75)

☐ **VOLUME I**
692 THE ONLY CHARITY, Sara Seale
785 THE SURGEON'S MARRIAGE
Kathryn Blair
806 THE GOLDEN PEAKS, Eleanor Farnes

☐ **VOLUME II**
649 KATE OF OUTPATIENTS
Elizabeth Gilzean
774 HEATHERLEIGH, Essie Summers
853 SUGAR ISLAND, Jean S. Macleod

☐ **VOLUME III**
506 QUEEN'S COUNSEL, Alex Stuart
760 FAIR HORIZON, Rosalind Brett
801 DESERT NURSE, Jane Arbor

☐ **VOLUME IV**
501 DO SOMETHING DANGEROUS
Elizabeth Hoy
816 THE YOUNGEST BRIDESMAID
Sara Seale
875 DOCTOR DAVID ADVISES, Hilary Wilde

☐ **VOLUME V**
721 SHIP'S SURGEON, Celine Conway
862 MOON OVER THE ALPS, Essie Summers
887 LAKE OF SHADOWS, Jane Arbor

☐ **VOLUME VI**
644 NEVER TO LOVE, Anne Weale
650 THE GOLDEN ROSE, Kathryn Blair
814 A LONG WAY FROM HOME, Jane Fraser

**Just Published**
($1.95 per volume)

☐ **VOLUME XXXI**
693 TOWARDS THE SUN, Rosalind Brett
743 THE HOUSE ON FLAMINGO CAY
Anne Weale
813 THE WEDDING DRESS, Mary Burchell

☐ **VOLUME XXXII**
526 WHEN YOU HAVE FOUND ME
Elizabeth Hoy
826 DOCTOR'S ASSISTANT, Celine Conway
854 TENDER CONQUEST, Joyce Dingwell

☐ **VOLUME XXXIII**
596 HOPE FOR THE DOCTOR
Margaret Malcolm
845 FLOWER FOR A BRIDE, Barbara Rowan
886 BACHELORS GALORE, Essie Summers

☐ **VOLUME XXXIV**
586 CAMERON OF GARE, Jean S. Macleod
753 DOCTOR MAX, Eleanor Farnes
823 DEAR ADVERSARY, Kathryn Blair

☐ **VOLUME XXXV**
840 THE HOUSE OF ADRIANO
Nerina Hilliard
870 THE DARK STRANGER, Sara Seale
884 NURSE AT CAP FLAMINGO
Violet Winspear

☐ **VOLUME XXXVI**
685 DOCTOR MARK TEMPLE
Elizabeth Gilzean
846 ABOVE THE CLOUDS, Esther Wyndham
885 AT THE VILLA MASSINA, Celine Conway

---

# FREE!

## Harlequin Romance Catalogue

Here is a wonderful opportunity to read many of the Harlequin Romances you may have missed.

The HARLEQUIN ROMANCE CATALOGUE lists hundreds of titles which possibly are no longer available at your local bookseller. To receive your copy, just fill out the coupon below, mail it to us, and we'll rush your catalogue to you!

Following this page you'll find a sampling of a few of the Harlequin Romances listed in the catalogue. Should you wish to order any of these immediately, kindly check the titles desired and mail with coupon.

# Have You Missed Any of These
# Harlequin Romances?

All books are 60c. Please use the handy order coupon.
BB